THE OLD MAN'S L

M000205298

"As earthy as the rocky hill soil and pure as a pristine mountain stream, author Michael Reisig, in *The Old Man's Letters*, cuts directly to the core of humanity with this new collection. He gives us a spontaneous, full-throated belly laugh, but more often makes us stop, draw in a sharp breath and exhale quickly. A gem of a collection."
> -- Maylon Rice, *The Northwest Arkansas Times*

"You'll laugh so hard, you'll embarrass yourself--and you'll be heart-touched to silence."
> -- Scott Bourns, editor, *The Mena Star*

"...Jake Strider delivers a timeless narrative of acute observations leavened with anecdotal humor. He's an old codger with an attitude, and his perceptions of modern life in the rural South are dead-on."
> -- Sarah McNeil, *The Jonesboro Sun*

"Forget Chicken Soup. This is the meat and potatoes of Middle America!"
> -- Best-selling author, Richard Noone

"Reisig's 'old Jake Strider' is one of the great story-tellers of a passing generation--blending keen observation with the art of the yarn, and he spins them beautifully."
> -- Tom McDonald, editor, *The Log Cabin Democrat*

"A book for rural America to brandish and cherish. Excellent!"
> --*The Ouachita Writers Guild*

"We thought tall tales were from Texas, until we met this Arkansas wit who moved in and tickled our fancy while teaching us modern folklore. Old Jake Strider is a new-found friend."
> -- Lyn Blackmon, *The Texarkana Gazette*

Clear Creek Publishing

P.O. Box 1081

Mena, AR 71953

(501) 394-4992

ISBN 0-9651240-4-5

Cover design by Powell Graphics

Thanks to Bonnie Lee and Verla Huckaby for editing and proofing.
Special thanks to Billie Wright for the "Being a Christian" piece.

Author's note: This is a work of fiction. With the exception of actual personages identified as such, the characters and incidents in this book are the products of my imagination and bear no relation to any person or event in real life.

THE
OLD MAN'S
LETTERS

By Michael Reisig

TABLE OF CONTENTS

TABLE OF CONTENTS

JAKE STRIDER

He was an old man. His gnarled hands, like river bottom willows, clutched the knob of his cane as he perched on the edge of a frayed, nylon lounge chair on the sun deck of Rich Mountain Retirement Home, gazing at a vee of geese as they made their way across a mottled, fall sky. He wore his crowned and thinning hair rakishly long, combed straight back and tucked behind his ears. His skin was the color of sun-bleached mangrove roots. Pale and withered, still as a stone, he sat staring at the distant birds.

He turned and looked up as he heard me approach, and smiled, his ancient face dropping 20 years in an instant. His eyes touched and held mine. Those bright, hazel orbs took me by surprise. They didn't belong to an old man; they sparkled with wit and charm, radiating such humor and mischievousness. Yet there was a sageness there, purchased, no doubt, by the triumphs and the tragedies of his life. In an instant, those eyes shouted volumes about the man: he had been a lover and a rogue, a gambler who had bet it all. He had won and lost more times than most of us had played. He was kind, but not stupid, and there was a strength about him that mirrored tenacity and a core of willpower. I was immediately looking forward to our conversation.

My editor at *The Mena Star* had assigned me to interview Jake Strider for the "Neighbor of the Week" section of our local paper--a 1,200-word article on the life of some local personality. The editor knew Strider. He had smiled knowingly, promising I wouldn't be bored with the fellow.

I introduced myself, and the old man reciprocated. His voice carried the gravelly timber of distant summer thunder. "Jake Strider's the name, but just call me Strider, everyone else does," he said, sliding back into his rickety lawn chair and motioning me to another near him. We talked for a while of little things--the weather, crops, who was catching what out at the lake. I told him about my job at the newspaper and the books that I write. He spoke briefly of his son, who was in the military, and how he missed seeing him regularly. He mentioned his early days in Florida, and how, after all this time, he still couldn't get used to Arkansas winters. He told me about "the old folks home,"what days the food was fairly good, what nurses would let him pinch them on the rear, and which of the old ladies on the sun deck were still "looking for love in all the wrong places."

He was a character, there was no question, but there was an erudite understanding of life that emanated from him. The bravado and the impetuousness of youth were gone, and in their place was the honesty of experience, and knowledge one can only buy with time. He moved with a deliberateness and a grace that was provided by a long-time confidence in himself--a certainty of who and where he was in life.

I was about to bring the conversation around to the story I wanted, when the phone on the table next to him buzzed insistently.

"A gift from my son," he said. "Makes it easier for him to get me when he has a chance." He picked it up, listening for a moment. "Yeah, this is Mr.Strider." He listened for a few more seconds, looked over at me and smiled impishly. He had one of the new portables that had a speaker phone button. He pressed it so we both could hear, and set it on the table.

"Hello, Hello? Mr. Streeder?" came a reedy voice from the other end. (A poor pronunciation of his name--it wasn't someone who knew him.) "Mr. Streeder, I'm Jeff Tanum of Acme Vinyl Home Siding. How are you today, sir?" (A salesman, and a bad one at that--he just told us right away what he sold without offering to give away anything free in the first sentence.) He was obviously a neophyte. Jake knew it, too. He looked at me and grinned like a spider who had just watched a fly whack into his web.

"Mr. Streeder, how would you like a--"

"Hold on, Jeff," said Strider. "I have to close the flap on the tent." He waited a few seconds. "There, that's better. If you don't get those flaps down tight, the wind just whistles through the canvas."

"Of the tent?" Jeff asked incredulously. "You're in a tent?"

"Sure thing," replied Strider. "I live in a tent. My parents were Arabs. I've lived in tents all my life; wouldn't have it any other way. In fact, I sell tents for a living. You wouldn't like to buy a tent, would you, Jeff? They're a little cool in the winter, but they're great in spring and summer--get you out of that stuffy apartment."

"You're kidding me..." Jeff replied hesitantly, "because I sell siding--"

"Heck no, Jeff," said Strider, really getting into the part. "Here, I'll hold the phone next to the flap so you can hear the wind." He picked up the phone and blew across the mouthpiece. "Well, what do you think, Jeff? How about a tent? I could get you into a good used one. If you're willing to move around a little you can camp at rest stops--never pay any rent."

"I, I don't think so, Mr. Streeder. I, I--"

"Think about it, Jeff. Just you and your dog on the open road, selling siding whereever you go. That's freedom. That's excitement!"

"I, I don't have a dog."

"Not to worry, Jeff, I've got a couple. I'll throw one in with the tent. He's a cute little fellow--got a small problem with worms right now, but that's easily fixed. I've got these suppositories--you just get him on your lap with his little ass in the air and--"

"I, I gotta go now, Mr. Streeder, my other phone is ringing."

"Wait, Jeff, don't hang up," said Strider. "I wouldn't normally do this, but you seem like an all right fellow. I'll give you the tent at half price, I'll throw in the dog and I'll sell you a good, low-mileage camel to carry everything. Camels are good, cheap transportation--used them all my life. They're gonna be big over here. They hobble right past every gas station, never need a tune-up. This one does have a bit of a nasty disposition; he spits at you a lot, and unfortunately he also has a small case of worms. But not to worry, I've got suppositories for him too. I'll admit, though, that he's a bit more of a challenge than the dog. Your best bet is to sneak up behind him and grab him by the *cahones*. When he screams, his tail automatically goes up, and that gives you your one and only shot--a three-second window of opportunity. Now, at this point, don't dawdle. You take your time with that wax bullet while squeezing the camel's privates and he's gonna kick the bejejees out of you. One last word of caution--don't ever attempt this after the camel has just eaten. Whatta you say, Jeff--a camel, a dog, and a tent for less than $500 bucks--a whole new life for you? Jeff?... Jeff?"

The line went dead.

Strider reached over and turned the phone off, chuckling. "I'm an old man," he said. "I have limited forms of entertainment, so sometimes I have to create my own. I got my name put on a couple of phone sales lists.

"There's no dignity in the business of being a phone jackal. They would offer you their sister as a bonus to make a sale, and they call all hours of the day and night. The trick is to compete with them on their own level. Be creative, beat them at their own game." He smiled again. "Play it right, and they're more fun than late night television."

Such was my introduction to Jake Strider.

THE OLD MAN'S LETTERS

Finally, Strider placed his cane between his knees and leaned forward, resting his hands on the tarnished oak knob."So you want a story, do you?" He smiled as I got out my small recorder and turned it on. "You've come to the well with a thimble young fellow, but I'll see if I can't give you an abbreviated, printable version of the life and times of Jake Strider."

He began to tell me about his travels and adventures, the remarkable people he had known. Lord, the stories he had stashed away--like photographs in a dusty old album. I let the recorder run and took an occasional note or two, but mostly I just listened.

Strider was born in California in 1920. He spent his childhood growing up in a small community just south of Sacramento. His folks moved to Saint Petersburg, Florida when he was 16. He graduated high school in Saint Pete, and for the next couple of years, worked as a guitarist--a talent he, "just sort of picked up."

World War II interrupted his musical career. He joined the service and eventually went into pilot training in the Army Air Corps. He ended up flying B17s in the European Theater for a couple of years.

"Got lucky--survived--got out in '46." he recalled with a wistful smile. "After the war, a friend and I decided we wanted to see the world--thought we'd start with Australia. Somewhere between getting our passports and packing our bags, it occurred to us we'd cut the finances a little close. Upon arrival in Sidney, we were going to have about $59. The two of us opted for a trip across these United States. We figured to be gone about six months. Turned out, we were on the road for the next seven years. It was one of the more memorable times of my life.

"My partner, Bill, and I spent a year in New Orleans, working as bartenders, chasing women. Then we headed up to Montana where we worked on a cattle ranch, chasing cattle for about a year--it was pretty country, but too lonely and too damned cold.

"Ended up in San Diego for a while, then slipped into Mexico--tried our hand at gold mining in the Sierra Madres--chased more women. One of them pretty senoritas caught Bill and he got married. Unfortunately, she had a bad temper and a penchant for knives. Bill decided to get out of Dodge before he came up missing parts. He got a Mexican divorce (found the local judge at the cantina--bought him three tequilas, paid him 10 pesos) and we hit the road again. When all was said and done, we ended up in the Florida Keys. Basically, it had everything we were originally going to Australia for-- beaches, clear waters, lovely women--and it was a hell of a lot closer. Turned out to be one of my better decisions this lifetime. We opened a small diving business--taking tourists out to the reef. It was almost the perfect occupation for us, and we settled into island life."

One of the white-smocked attendants at the retirement home passed by. Strider paused in his narration and asked if we could have a couple cups of coffee. The fellow nodded and returned moments later. Strider, while adding copious amounts of sugar to his black coffee, caught my glance. "What? I gotta watch my weight? I gotta worry about a little sugar it killing me?"

I just smiled. "It's your coffee."

He continued. "Eventually Bill found a gal from Wisconsin that caught his attention and he got married--this time for good. About a year later, I met a sweet young thing from Arkansas. She took me home with her to meet her folks, and I hardly left these hills again. We had a son, and he grew up strong and healthy. He did well with his studies, got a scholarship to college under the ROTC Program and became an officer in the Air Force. My wife died a couple of years ago--some strange affliction that even the doctors had trouble pronouncing. My son's job keeps him stationed in different places all over the world. That pretty much just left me here."

The afternoon wore on and he carried me back and forth across the passages of his life with the ease of a seasoned storyteller. His time on this spinning ball of dirt and water had been a collage of anecdotes--knee-slapping humorous, insightful, and touching. He had taken the orange of life and squeezed it dry--then eaten the pulp. When it was all said and done, I had the article I wanted--and then some. I finally excused myself with some reluctance. It had been a fascinating interview and an enjoyable afternoon.

As I drove away that day, I assumed my relationship with Strider was completed, but I was wrong. About a month after our interview, I got a box in the mail from Major Jim Strider, U.S. Air Force, Ramstein, Germany. Inside, I found dozens of letters that the old man had written to his son through the years. There was a note, saying the major had received a copy of the article I had done on his father and was impressed with my writing. He thought perhaps I might be interested in using the enclosed letters in some sort of publication.

I knew that Strider's wit and intelligence ran deeper and wider than most, but I doubted there was anything in that box that would be of use to me. Nonetheless, I decided to take a glance at a few of the letters in courtesy to Jim Strider. I read one, then another, then one more...Time closed in around me like a cocoon and I sat there for the next two hours--laughing out loud, and being heart-touched to silence. The old man's letters were an hilarious, insightful panorama of rural life. Many of the them were really stories about friends and acquaintances of his. Others posed poignant social and political points of view. Each one captured me.

When I had finished, I knew exactly what I wanted to do.

The following are Jake Strider's letters to his son, mostly in chronological order, beginning in the 1980s, and moving forward to the present. I've done very little editing. I have eliminated introductions and more personal conversation, keeping to the nexus of each correspondence, and I have provided each letter a heading for easier referencing.

At this writing Jake is still alive and well. He turned 80 in September.

Michael Reisig
Mena Star staff writer,
Mena, AR

NEIGHBORS

May 12, 1985

Today, the majority of the land in and around our area no longer consists of large ranches and farms, but is more a mosaic of small ownerships.

In years past, the only sound you heard from your neighbors was an occasional gunshot. Today many, if not most, homesteads are close enough together for you to hear your neighbors arguing over who was supposed to take out the trash. I don't care much for that. It's not what I came to Arkansas for.

The piece of property your mother and I recently purchased in Nunley is big enough to insulate us on three sides. The land bordering the north corner, however, is within a few hundred yards of the house, and it has recently come up for sale. We're not sure we can afford to buy the property, but we're a little concerned about having a Louisiana or Texas version of "The Honeymooners" settling in next to us. If the truth be known, I'm not sure I want anyone buying that land.

The other day I was preparing to mow our lawn when I saw a pick up truck stop on the road by the real estate sign at the edge of the north pasture. A man and a woman got out, talking, gesturing toward the property for sale. I decided I needed a plan. I slapped my hat on backwards, hopped on the mower and drove it out to where the people were standing.

"Afternoon," I said in my best hayseed dialect as I turned off the mower. "Couldn't help but notice you all stopped on the road. You folks got car problems? Anything I can do for y'all?"

"No," replied the man. "We're just looking at this piece of property."

"Yep, yep," I said, nodding my head like a cupie doll, "Pretty enough piece of land. It'd sure be nice to have neighbors again. The last folks were only there two months before they drove off with their trailer and put the place up for sale."

"Two months?" the fellow said. "How come?"

"Ticks, least that's what I heard. Ticks the size of golf balls. One of them unexplained phenomenons, like the lemmings. Huge things, suck a full-grown coon dog dry quicker than you can spit. Property's loaded with 'em. I guess it could have something to do with the toxic waste."

"Toxic waste?" the man said, his voice rising slightly.

"It's only a rumor, probably not a shred of truth to it. 'Course that could explain why the last owner lost all his hair and got all blotchy-looking."

At the mention of ticks and toxic waste, the woman was already shuffling backwards. The man held his ground, not ready to be intimidated yet. I moved into phase two. Without warning I put my fingers to my mouth and gave a loud whistle. The woman flinched like she'd been shot. On cue, Mac, my 140 pound Rottweiler came bounding toward us from the house. A dog that size running at you is an impressive sight. The woman was already moving around to her side of the truck and the door. The guy hesitantly took two steps backwards and rested his hand on the door handle. Grabbing Mac by the collar as he braked in front of the truck I said congenially, "Hope you folks like dogs. We raise a few of these fellas in the pens behind the house." (We don't, of course, but the statement had the desired effect.) "They don't usually get out," I added, "but if they do, just keep your cats and small children inside 'til we catch 'em."

"Yeah, real nice piece of property," I said again, "'cept when the creek floods."

"When the creek floods?" the man asked. "There's no creek on this property."

I smiled sagely. "You haven't seen it rain around here, buddy. What isn't hilltop is creek. I don't mind the water much but all them dern cottonmouths...."

"Snakes?" his wife said shrilly from the other side of the truck.

"I wouldn't worry about 'em, ma'am," I said. "The bite's not usually fatal. You'll swell up like a toad and turn purple as a bruised plum for a bit, and they may have to cut out a hunk of flesh where the fangs got you, but you'll be okay. Here, I'll show ya what a bite looks like," I said, reaching for my belt buckle. "I was answering the call of nature a couple months ago and one got me right on the ol' backside."

"No, No!" they replied in harmony, the woman retreating to her seat in the truck. The guy had opened his door and was standing behind it now, beginning to lose some of his composure.

"Not sure this is the piece we want," he said. "We're really just looking."

"Well, I'd be glad to walk you through it, show you where the boundaries are," I replied. "Pretty important that you know where your property lines, cause the fellas that own the land west of here grow some things in the woods they don't want people botherin' with, if you know what I mean."

"Maybe some other time," said the fellow as his wife dragged him into the cab. "But thanks for all your help, just the same."

"Anytime, anytime at all," I replied with a toothy grin. "Y'all come back, now."

Lord, I just hate myself when I get devious--but it's so much fun.

****

THE LOVE OF THE LAND

Aug. 4, 1985

When I was younger and my folks owned a small ranch in Kansas, I remember my mother good-naturedly chiding my father for always finding something to tinker with on the property, from checking the cattle, or mending a fence, to trimming a fruit tree. He would explain to her (and to me) that his love of the outdoors, and in particular, his affection for that small 40 acre square of earth with its gnarled oak trees, gentle, grassy knolls, and rugged, old barns struck a chord within him that satisfied his most intrinsic needs.

He was bonded to that land, welded to it like the roots of the trees that held the soil in place on the dusty summer hillsides. He'd walk the fields until sunset, mending, pruning and sometimes just placidly observing the wonders of the seasons nature provided him, and there was always a quiet sense of peace about him when he came in for the evening. I didn't understand that then, but I do now.

As you know, a few months ago we bought a piece of property just outside of Mena, 15 acres of tree-shrouded, rolling hills, and pasture as green as any Irish clover. A small clear-water creek wanders through the center, close enough to the porch of the farmhouse that you can hear the water dancing on the rocks in the still evenings. Now I understand what my father felt.

There are many different kinds of ownership, from possession for the simple sake of having, which satisfies only ego, to the deep-seated innate love of something that doesn't simply belong to us, but that we belong to. Some things we possess and some things possess us. Every time I plant a new tree on that precious piece of land that I belong to, I understand my father better.

In the evenings, when the sun has breached the tall pines that stand like sentinels at the edge of the pasture, and the whippoorwills greet the coming night, I watch the fireflies make magic in the still darkness, and eventually I hear your mother, Bonnie, calling to me from the front porch.

As I begin to walk back toward the house, I am once again reminded how much I've become like that gentle man who gave me his love of the land.

****

ATTENTION SHOPPERS

Sept. 19, 1985

Every once in a while something happens that is just so much better than anything I could invent, I just have to shake my head in wonder and smile in appreciation of the devil's sense of humor. Now this story is true, I swear. It may however, have been embellished somewhat by the time it reached me, but it was so good by then that it required little artistic license on my part. This is the tale as I heard it....

A woman went grocery shopping at one of the stores in Polk County, one of those super-sized places that ends with a "Mart." When she finished her shopping she returned to the car, put her groceries in the back seat, got in behind the wheel and relaxed for a moment while waiting for her son, who was still in the store. Time passed, it was a hot day....

A little while later, a fellow who had just left the store was walking through the parking lot when he heard someone cry out. He looked over and observed the lady behind the wheel of her car, writhing and moaning loudly, holding the back of her head with her hands. He rushed over and knocked on her window, asking if he could be of assistance. She--or he--managed to get the door open, but at that point the lady was nearing hysterics.

"Help me! Help me!" she cried. "Call the police! I've been shot in the back of the head!" The man's first response was to reach forward to examine the wound, but the lady pulled back screaming, "No! No! Don't touch me! I'm holding my brains in with my hands! Please, please, call the police now!"

Who would have ever thought? An innocent soul shot while waiting at a store in our quiet little county! What is this world coming to? The man, quite unnerved, dashed off to the pay phone and called for an ambulance. Within minutes the ambulance and the police arrived, prepared for the worst, searching for the sniper, the point of entry, and looking for the blood...but there wasn't any. Nope, no crazed gunman, no shattered windows or rendered flesh, no gore. When they calmed the woman down enough to examine her, they discovered that while she waited for her son, a package of refrigerated biscuits in the backseat had warmed to critical mass and exploded, the contents of which slammed her in the back of the head. Yes, you heard right, struck down in her prime by a biscuit-bullet, a gooey projectile of Pillsbury's best that had smacked her hard enough to jiggle her eyeballs. (I swear I'm not making this up.) Those precious brains she was attempting to keep from draining out of her cranium were nothing more than the Doughboy's buttermilks!

Now I have to wonder what was going through the lady's mind (or what was left of it, as she perceived it) as she attempted to squeeze the biscuit/brains back into her head. Did it occur to her at any time that she was remarkably lucid for having the better part of her grey matter oozing through her fingers and dripping down the headrest? Did she notice at all that her brains seemed a little chilled? Well, these questions and many more we'll probably never have answers to, disappointing as it is. But I felt the tale itself was worth the telling.

In closing, let me leave you with the moral of this little story. It just goes to show you that you have to be careful out there, because calamity can rise up at anytime and strike you when you yeast expect it....

THE GREAT TURKEY HUNT

March 5, 1986

Ah, here it is--spring turkey season again. The aroma of damp earth on a misty morning, the crisp crackle of leaves underfoot, the heavy, satisfying feel of a cold weapon in your hands, and the startling first sight of your prey: these are many of the reasons we hunt. But, even with all the odds in our favor, every once in a while something goes awry.

I have a hunting buddy who lives in Mount Ida. We'll call him Rodge. Now, Rodge was wrapped a little loose before he went to Nam. The field trips to Cambodia didn't help. Although he loves the outdoors (he's one of the few people I know who wishes the deer could shoot back), Rodge's approaches to the primitive instinct sports are a little unconventional, and the tangents he goes off on occasionally land him in trouble.

His idea of fishing is a baitcasting rod, 20-pound test line, and a grenade. He likes guns with sufficient stopping power to disable a bulldozer, and he owns an armory that would make the National Guard envious--or worried.

A while back, Rodge called and asked me if I'd like to go turkey hunting with him.

"With guns?" I asked.

"Yeah, sure, with guns," he replied. "Grenades mess 'em up too much."

Now, knowing Rodge's history with this sort of enterprise, I should have said no, but I really wanted a turkey for the larder, and the season was nearing an end. My primal instincts got the better of me, and I agreed, though my concern escalated when Rodge assured me we would get a turkey, "'cause he had a plan...."

The following morning, just as the first rays of the sun began to edge the darkness, we were already in position deep in the National Forest. Rodge had brought a large duffel bag with him, but when I asked him what was in it, he wouldn't tell me. He just smiled and said it was part of "the plan." He was maybe 20 yards from me and I could hear him rustling around in the darkness, but I couldn't see him. In the distance, I heard an old tom call. A few moments later, I heard my partner use his diaphragm caller, the kind that fits in the roof of your mouth. I looked over and suddenly, out of the gloom, came Rodge.

My jaw dropped. I didn't know whether to laugh out loud, or shoot him and put him out of his misery. Crazy ol' Rodge was dressed in a giant turkey suit, complete with beak protruding over his forehead, full-feathered wings that his arms fit into, beige-colored tights on his legs, and clawed tennis shoes. One arm tucked his gun to his side. The surprising part was how darned much he looked like a turkey!

"Wetti ool, uh?" he said.

"Take the diaphragm out of your mouth."

"Pretty cool, huh?" he repeated. "I'll be just another big ol' turkey, get those suckers to walk right up to me."

Closer, now, the old tom gobbled again. "Get down!" I whispered tensely. "Behind that log."

As Rodge settled in behind a giant fallen oak, he put his diaphragm back in his mouth and called again. The turkey answered, insistent. Everything was going perfectly--it looked like a piece of cake. I should have known better.

It seems there were a couple of factors we were unaware of. First, two other hunters were moving in to the west of us, stalking what they thought were a pair of turkeys calling to each other. Secondly, was the nest of fire ants that Rodge had sat down on: ants that were, at that moment, crawling into his feathers and leggin's. Fire ants are crafty little creatures. It's almost like they wait until they're all in place, then bite on cue.

All of a sudden Rodge grunted and his eyes bulged. He stood straight up and stumbled over the log, his arms flapping, doing some kind of demented turkey jig. The turkey caller caught in his throat and he started cackling and gobbling, performing some of the finest turkey calling I'd ever heard, but I was sure that dance thing was going to scare the bird.

Before I could yell at him to get back down, I heard someone call from the other side of the clearing, "Look Jeb! There's the biggest goll-derned turkey I ever seen. Get 'em! Shoot that son-of-a-gun!"

The roar of a shotgun shattered the stillness of the morning, and a patch of feathers on Rodge's haunches exploded. He did a standing broad jump of about 15 feet (probably a record of some sort), coughing up the diaphragm as he shrieked, spitting it about 25 feet (probably another record). Rodge dashed for the woods, zig-zagging, screaming and flapping while shotgun blasts chewed the bark off trees around him. I kept my head down until the shooting stopped.

When the smoke cleared, Rodge was gone. The other hunters had disappeared as well, probably still searching for the Loch Ness turkey. Two hours later, I found Rodge in the back of the car, nursing a load of birdshot-- the turkey suit gone, left in the woods. I looked at him.

"Don't say a word," he said. "Just take me home. I want a beer and a TV dinner, in that order."

"Would that be turkey and dressing?" I asked with a smile.

****

TOURISTS AND INDIGENOUS INSECTS

July 19,1986

Having come from South Florida to Arkansas, I was immediately aware of several of the more obvious differences between the two states. Take tourists, for instance. In Florida there is a love-hate relationship with tourists: nobody really likes them, but everybody needs their money. Here, in typical Arkansas fashion, tourists are made to feel quite welcome. Oh, there are a few glances and a chuckle or two when they ask directions to the Wa-chita River, or when they come back from walking in the woods and they're doing the Arkansas Chigger Dance: take one step forward and scratch your ankle, take two steps back and itch your ass.

Chiggers. Now those are one of Mother Nature's most contrary creatures. They sort of remind me of Arkansas' version of the Yeti or Sasquatch: everybody talks about them but nobody's really sure what they look like, and one encounter with them is generally enough to satisfy a person's curiosity.

This reminds me of a friend of mine who lives north of DeQueen, just off Highway 71, in Southwestern Arkansas. You could say he was taken more than most by this Yeti/Sasquatch thing. One day he drove to Little Rock and bought a gorilla suit at a costume store. Every once in a while, late at night, he used to get drunk, put the suit on and wait in the woods by the highway near his house. When he saw a pair of lights approaching he'd lumber out onto the road, hands swinging by his knees, then stop in front of the car and raise his arms menacingly. About the time the wide-eyed driver began to slam on his brakes, my drunken buddy would lurch into the woods laughing like a hyena! On occasion, one or two of the more observant victims would question what a Sasquatch was doing carrying a bottle of Jack Daniels, but even so, the phenomenon began to gain notoriety.

Eventually he had to give up his little late night charade; the Sasquatch investigators showed up with infra-red cameras and tranquilizer dart guns, trying to capture what the local press had labeled as the ArkaMan, the Southwest's missing link!

Those of us who knew hadn't the heart to tell them they were dealing with a sotted local wearing a monkey suit and a Tina Turner wig.

You know what else I like about Arkansas? I like the mosquitos here. That is to say I like the fact that they look like mosquitos, and there aren't clouds of them like in Florida. In Southern Florida the mosquitos are bigger than Arkansas hummingbirds. They laugh at bug repellent, in fact, I think they developed a taste for it. They're so big, the only way to stop them is with a 410 shotgun and #8 shot. (Floridians have learned, however, that it is far better to use this method of repulsion outside of their homes.)

Speaking of guns, that's another one of the big differences between rural Arkansas and South Florida. You're not allowed to carry a gun in your car in Florida, but you need one. In rural Arkansas nobody needs a gun, but everybody's got one in the window of their pickup--I love this place.

In closing, I'd like to tell you what I really appreciate about Arkansas as opposed to much of the country. The genuine Arkansans that I have met here have not forgotten the value of integrity, both personally and on a community level.

The best example I can give you is the guy that owns the fruit stand in front of his house on Highway 88. He leaves his fruit in the stand, day and night. He leaves $20 in change in a tin can on the counter. There's a note on the can that reads, "If I'm not here, help yourself and put your money in the can. Make your own change."

I told him, "If this was Miami, the first night you left that stand alone, the fruit would be gone, the money would be gone, and the next time anyone saw that stand it would be painted a garish yellow and somebody would be selling burritos out of it on Biscayne Boulevard!"

Twenty dollars in a tin can, for goodness sake, on a well traveled road. He told me that in all the years he's been selling fruit, he's never had a dime stolen.

At the risk of sounding like a Burger King commercial, I just gotta say it again, "I love this place!"

****

ILLEGAL GARDENS AND SLEIGH RIDES

Oct. 13, 1986

Ah, fall is in the air: cool winds ruffle the trees, sheets of leaves cascade to the ground in gentle billows. The sweet autumn fragrance of plants in final bloom fills the air: moonflowers, jasmine, and gee, is that marijuana I smell?

Yes, it's that time again when the growers of Arkansas' number one cash crop discreetly begin their harvest, gambling that they'll stay one step ahead of the jailer.

As perilous an enterprise as it may be, there are still a handful of audacious souls out there who just can't resist the smell of green--in whatever form. And let's face it, they probably come by their penchant for the illegitimate quite honestly. Seems to me it wasn't long ago that moonshining was pretty popular in these parts.

Now, I don't know much about pot, and I certainly never inhaled it, I can assure you of that. But I do know a good tale when I hear one, and the other day I was in just the right place at the right time to be privy to a yarn.

I was sitting in a quiet little tavern just over the state line, washing down that county road dust with a cold one, when I overheard the fellow at the table next to me telling a story.

Seems a couple friends of his, two brothers, had grown a patch of pot up on a mountainside in a remote area of Oklahoma. Two or three hundred yards below the garden ran a wide swathe of the Mountain Fork River, which supplied their water.

Lem and Larry had carefully nurtured their crop through summer and into fall, but only days before harvest an early norther had rolled through and deposited three inches of snow on everything. Now they had to get their crop off the mountain, pronto. Lem, the smarter of the two, suggested they use an old three-man sled, and tow it down the mountain. Without thinking about it much, Larry agreed, but then thinking wasn't one of Larry's strong points. Truth was, when it came to intellect, about the only difference between Larry and a Tyson chicken was the feathers.

Well, bright and early the next day the two guerilla gardeners bounced their way down the old logging road in their battered pickup, stopping at the edge of the river. There they unloaded the sled, pruning shears and garbage bags, then began climbing the hill. By mid-morning they had the pot cut, bagged and tied to the sled.

They had been so busy working they failed to notice the two county sheriff's cars that pulled up behind their truck, and the handful of deputies that spread out and began climbing the hill. You see, the day before, the boys in the surveillance helicopter had spotted the neat little patch of pot laying stark green against the white snow of the mountain.

As the deputies silently climbed the hill, the unsuspecting duo prepared to depart. Larry suggested to Lem that they try sitting on top of the bundles of pot and riding the sleigh slowly down the mountain. Lord knows why, but Lem agreed (which doesn't do much for Lem's credibility as the smart one). About then things took a decidedly downhill turn for the bunco brothers.

Larry sat on the front of the sled, holding the steering rope like a bull rider just before the gate opens. Lem gave them a push and swung himself up, straddling the bundles in the back, holding onto one of the ropes that bound the garbage bags of pot to the sled.

At first, Larry was laughing and yelling, "Mush! Mush!" to imaginary dogs while Lem sat behind him smiling, pleased as peaches that his little plan was going so well. Sad to say, neither of them remembered how steep that old hill got just past the ridge... In a few moments they'd gone from coasting leisurely to zipping along at an alarming speed. Trees were suddenly blurring by. Larry, eyes bulging like goose eggs, was edging rapidly towards panic and starting to make little whining noises in the back of his throat. Lem tried to dig his heels into the snow to slow them down, but his feet barely reached the ground. The sled was careening down the hill like a demented version of the Batmobile, bouncing and jagging at breakneck speed. Larry's whine had burbled into a full-fledged shriek. Just when it looked like things couldn't get any worse, they saw the police.

They shot through the line of startled deputies, yipping and yelling like a Jamaican bobsled team. Heck, at that point either of the plummeting pair would gladly have traded a jail cell for the sleigh ride from hell. But they were not to be so lucky. They were three-quarters of the way down the mountain and miraculously still on the sled. That was the good news. The bad news was the raging, rain-swollen river and the cliff that lay in wait not fifty yards ahead.

Lem decided he'd had all the fun he could handle and stood up to jump, but at that moment they shot under a tree and a low branch took him off the sled like he'd been swatted by the hand of God. That left crazy Larry, the sleigh, the pot, and the river, in that order. Screaming like a banshee and frozen to the reins, Larry shot across the road, over the last of the snow-covered precipice and sailed off the cliff looking like Slim Pickins riding the bomb in *Dr. Strangelove*. Behind him, the deputies watched in slack-jawed amazement as he flew a good fifty feet out over the river and landed with a splash in the rolling torrent of brown water.

Nobody ever found the sled or the pot. Well, at least nobody reported it. Lem was taken into custody right there. Larry was found about nightfall, five miles down river, soaked to the bone, mud-spattered and shivering like a wet puppy. I guess it just goes to show, crime doesn't pay.

In the end, though, the police had to let them go; there was no evidence. What could they charge them with, failure to yield on a runaway sleigh? It didn't matter, the bunco brothers had experienced enough, they were going straight. I heard they changed their names to Gonzales, took the government test and became U.S. Postal employees.

Don't ya just love this place? America!

****

ROTTWEILERS AND RABBITS

Feb. 22, 1987

One of the things I've come to love about Arkansas is the remarkable variety of animals that abide in our woods and fields. From my front porch I can watch a daily panoply of acrobatic squirrels, myopic armadillos, an early morning rabbit or two and even an occasional deer.

The one creature in my household that finds all this more fascinating than me is Mac, my Rottweiler. Although a formidable fellow at 140 pounds, he has a gentle nature and the personality of a curious child. The difference between him and the local junkyard dog is that I have raised Mac as a companion, and he has rewarded my efforts tenfold. He loves to chase everything; he has yet to catch anything. It's not for lack of ability, he just figures if he starts catching things, word would get around and no one would want to play anymore. I really believe that's exactly what he thinks. He's that smart.

A while back I decided to teach him to fetch. I got his ball and threw it out on the lawn. Mac looked up at me, then out to the ball, but he didn't go get it. I went and picked up the ball, brought it back and showed it to him. He took it out of my hand and with a swing of his massive head, tossed it out into the grass. Then he looked up at me, like what are you waiting for, go get it. So, grumbling about stupid dogs, I went and got the ball and brought it back. He took it out of my hand, threw it again and looked at me, waiting. I'm a pretty smart fellow. It wasn't long before I figured out who was training whom. I went over to his ball and kicked it as far as I could, then I went in the house.

Mac and a local rabbit have become buddies of sorts. I'm sure it's a somewhat tenuous understanding, based on mutual entertainment, but it's an agreement nonetheless. Nearly every morning I'll come out onto the porch and see Mac laying in the grass, and the rabbit munching clover not fifteen feet from him. After a while the rabbit gets bored and begins popping up and down, looking over at the dog. That's the signal for the game to start. The rabbit jumps up, Mac clamors to his feet, and the chase is on. There's a good hundred yards of lawn between the house and the woods. It's just too long a dash for my lazy Rottweiler. Three quarters of the way through the race Mac lumbers to a halt. Just slightly ahead, the rabbit screeches to a stop and looks back, waiting for the dog to catch his breath. It's an impatient rabbit. If Mac doesn't get it together quickly enough, the bunny bounces back a few yards and stares at the dog with anxious disdain. I'm almost certain I've seen him stick out his tongue a couple of times, but I wouldn't swear to it. Soon after, the chase continues, until Mr. Cottontail disappears into the underbrush, leaving Mac huffing and puffing and sniffing at the edge of the brambles. It's a wonderful routine, and coffee in hand, your mother and I try to catch the show as often as we can.

This reminds me of a Yorkie named "Dukes" that I once had when I lived in Florida. Lord, that dog loved to swim. You couldn't draw a bath without having to fight to keep him out of the water. I'm convinced his mother must have had more than a passing fancy for Labradors.

Above and beyond his penchant for the water, Dukes had a remarkable sense of humor, a streak of mischievousness about him. When I took him to the beach, he would watch for snorklers bobbing gently in the clear waters along the shoreline. Dukes would spot a close one and swim out to them quietly, using the dog paddle (which was his favorite stroke, although his Australian crawl and his backstroke were fairly proficient). He would virtually sneak up on the unsuspecting tourist paddler, whose attentions were drawn to the coral sand bottom and whose sense of hearing was muted by the water. Swimming up silently, he would suddenly surge in and nip the hapless tourist on the ear.

Imagine if you will, you're visiting Florida for the first time, from Wisconsin, or Idaho, or even Arkansas. You're out there floating in all this water, you're having a good time, but you can't seem to get that disconcerting da da da da music of *Jaws* out of your mind, and you keep flashing back on all the Discovery Channel shark shows you've seen recently. Now about that time, when you least expect it, something wet and furry slides up against you and nips your ear. Well, I've seen tourists come straight out of the water like they'd been zapped by a cattle prod, masks filled with water, eyes bulging like a beached sea bass. I've seen them walk across that shallow water a good thirty or forty feet, flippers churning like something out of a Daffy Duck cartoon, before they even look back. Dukes would be out there just treading water and smiling....

I guess the point I'm trying to make is that I've had some wonderfully clever dogs in my life. But the truth is, I made them that way. The more latitude you give an animal to be intelligent, the more intelligent it will be. The more attention and effort you put into your relationship with an animal, the more that creature will become your friend, companion and protector, and the more entertaining that relationship will become.

The world of science, in all it's arrogance, has only just conceded (January issue, *Time Magazine*) what every loving pet owner has known all along; that animals have emotions, react to circumstance intelligently, and yes, they reason. Heck, I could have saved those scientists a lot of trouble by just taking them to the beach with me and Dukes one afternoon.

Well, that's about all I have time for today. I can hear Mac scratching on the door in the living room. He wants out to get the paper. It's Sunday, and he likes me to read him the comics....

****

BEING A CHRISTIAN

April 3, 1987

Being a Christian, nowadays, is more popular than ever. But it seems to me, with a lot of folks, there's a good gap between saying you're a Christian and behaving like one. A friend of mine sent me a little piece about living up to the letter of Christianity (what it means to be a real Christian) and I thought I'd pass it along to you.

His name was Bill. He had long, wild hair, wore a T-Shirt with holes in it, jeans, and a battered pair of tennis shoes. That was pretty much his wardrobe for the entire four years I knew him in college. He was brilliant, in an esoteric fashion--intuitive, but naive. He became a Christian while going to college.

Across the street from the school was an upscale, very conservative church. They wanted to develop a ministry to the students, but weren't sure how to go about it.

One day, Bill decides to attend their service. He walks in--no shoes, jeans, his T-shirt, disheveled hair. The service had already started, so Bill begins to walk down the isle looking for a seat. But the church was packed, not a space in a pew. (And in truth, few were anxious to squeeze together to accommodate the scruffy-looking young man.) Several people were beginning to look uncomfortable, but no one said anything. Bill gets closer and closer to the pulpit, and when he realizes there are no seats, he simply squats down on the carpet. (Perfectly acceptable behavior for a college fellowship, but you can bet it had never happened in that church before.) The tension in the air is almost tangible.

About that time, the minister realizes that, from way at the back of the church, a deacon is slowly making his way toward Bill. The Deacon is in his 80s, has silver-grey hair, a three-piece suit, and a gold pocket watch--a Godly man, very elegant, very dignified. He walks with a cane, and as he starts toward the boy, everyone is saying to themselves, *You can't blame him for what he's going to do. How can you expect a man of his age and background to understand some college kid sitting on the floor.*

It takes a long time for the old man to reach the boy. The church is utterly silent except for the clicking of the man's cane. All eyes are focused on the scene. The people are thinking, *The minister can't even preach the sermon until the deacon does what he has to do.*

Suddenly, the elderly man lets his cane drop to the floor. With great difficulty, he lowers himself and sits down next to Bill, to worship with him, so he won't be alone. Emotion rolls over the entire congregation like a summer wind across a wheat field.

When the minister gains control, he says, "What I'm about to preach, you will never remember. What you have just witnessed, you will never forget."

People learn more about God from what they see in their lives, rather than what they hear from our lips.

****

WIVES AND HOUNDS

Sept. 14,1987

A few weeks ago, the local paper ran a picture of a fellow and his champion hunting dogs. It reminded me of a couple of stories about friends of mine, their dogs, and their wives.

My buddy, Willie, has eight or ten coon dogs that he keeps outside, and a couple more that are special to his heart which he allows in the house. One of his pet hounds had managed to get worms, which isn't all that unusual around here. Willie's wife was going into town for groceries and vitamins and volunteered to pick up the medicine for the dog.

Will and his wife take a lot of vitamin supplements, having reached an age where hedging your bet on longevity becomes a consideration. Willie said he'd pretty much forgotten about the worm medicine after his wife said she'd take care of it. He had important things to worry about, he'd lost his reading glasses and had to get into town to order a new pair, and hunting season was only a week away. Preparation for the hunt took precedence and Willie forgot to get his glasses.

Each morning Willie would get his ritual cup of coffee and shake himself out a vitamin from each of the bottles on the counter. During the week, he noticed that his wife had purchased a new, larger gelatin capsule that could only be vitamin E (he couldn't read the label without his glasses), so he dutifully took two and gulped them down with the other supplements.

It was near the end of the week when old Will heard his wife complaining from the kitchen about the nearly empty bottle of worm medicine. "They sure don't give you many of these pills for the price," she said as she turned to him with the container he thought was vitamin E.

Well, they called the vet, and the doctor said it would probably be okay, and that Willie was probably safe from internal parasites for the next three months. Will, with the exception of a new-found attraction to tree trunks and dog biscuits, suffered no ill effects from the incident.

I had a another buddy who lived in Glenwood. He had a wife and a handful of hunting dogs. He really loved those dogs. Eventually his preoccupation with hunting and hounds led to a particularly bitter divorce.

A week before the national field trials, in which he had entered his best dog, his estranged wife stopped by the house while he was in town. She took a bottle of Neet hair remover and smeared it all over his number one hound, from his nose to the tip of his tail. But she didn't stop there. No, this was an angry woman. She went into the house, poured out most of his shampoo container in the shower, then filled it up again with a second bottle of Neet.

Well, for the first few days my friend and his dog looked like they'd acquired a horrendous case of mange. Hair fell out in clumps. The dog scratched and whimpered. My buddy shampooed time and again, trying to get rid of whatever it was that was plaguing him. The shampoo ran down his body and took off hair in places that made him look more amusing than his wife had ever hoped for. The hound looked like a forty pound Chihuahua.

By the time the field trials came up, there wasn't a hair left on either one of them. They were both disqualified for being way too shiny-looking and causing too much laughter in the audience.

For you fellows who have hounds and wives, I suppose the moral of these stories is that you need to pay attention to your wife and your dog, probably in that order.

SNAKE BASHING

Jan. 18,1988

It's safe to say that the average rural American has little love for snakes. Generally, when it comes to an encounter between the two, the snakes get the worst of it. Snake bashing is almost a bona fide rural pastime, falling somewhere between family entertainment and a backcountry sport. It's all but become an Arkansas art form.

There's a variety of approaches to snake-bashing. Each person seems to have their favorite weapon. Hoes and shovels are popular, claw hammers and machetes work well for the braver souls (you have to get close), and shotguns are an old standby. But of them all, the trusty automobile may be the most widely accepted implement of destruction when it comes to these scaly denizens.

There's an awful lot of folks who just can't resist running over a snake if it happens to be crossing the road and in their path. I was driving quietly along a back road the other day, when I watched the motorist in front of me deliberately cross into the oncoming lane in order to run over a luckless reptile slithering across the blacktop. It reminded me of a story.

There was this older couple with a home just off Highway 8 East who recognized the growing popularity of snake squashing. They owned a wrecker service, but business had been slow for them for some time, so they devised a method of entertaining passing motorists and picking up a few bucks in the process. Old Jeb got himself a spin-casting fishing rod with clear, monofilament line. Belinda, his wife, found a snake, bashed him just enough to be dead but not messy, and tied the end of the monofilament line around the reptile's head.

Like so many of the older homes in the country, their house was only a few yards from the road. The front porch faced the blacktop. Jeb would cast the snake out onto the road. Then he and Belinda would settle back in their rockers and wait for a car to approach. As soon as the driver spotted the snake, Jeb would start to reel (with a little rod tip action to increase the temptation). There weren't many motorists that could resist the action Jeb could give that snake. Hardly a day passed that a couple didn't run plumb off the road and into the ditch, trying to squash a snake that was long past caring. The wrecker business suddenly became quite good.

Every third or fourth day, Belinda would bash a fresh snake, because after being dragged across the highway 50 or 60 times and run over a couple more, the reptiles would begin to lose their life-like action (as they say in the fishing industry).

Jeb and Belinda eventually moved to Iowa to be with their children, and I guess the snake fishing/wrecker business came quietly to an end. I heard the story third or fourth-hand, and don't know exactly how much to believe, but it's an interesting tale and it certainly gives one food for thought.

The next time you spot that snake as you're driving along, you'd better look for the monofilament line before you head pell-mell after it. And take a glance at the closest house to make sure there isn't some guy sitting on the porch, reeling to beat the band and laughing his fool head off.

****

GUNS, PLANES, AND GOVERNMENT CLAIMS

Aug.26,1988

Just for fun, let's lambaste the government today. There's such a wealth of material here I hardly know where to begin, but what say we start with the truth in government statements.

Most of us have come to realize that when someone from the government shows up at your front door and says, "Trust me, I'm here to help you," you're probably in deep muckety-muck.

Let's examine for a moment these words, "trust me." They carry a whole bundle of negative connotations, from seedy salesmen and shady deals, to supposedly mailed checks and unilaterally pleasing sexual encounters. Still, it's a very popular bureaucratic phrase.

"We're here to help you." Hmmmm... That's another dandy. If you're not a foreign national, or on welfare (or both), when was the last time the government "helped you?"

So it is generally with some trepidation that we face encounters with the government. This brings me to the little tale I have for you today: the story of an innocent's blunder into bureaucratic barbed wire. True story, cross my heart.

A few months ago I had to attend a three-day seminar in Little Rock. Now, you know I lived in South Florida for quite a while before moving here. Even so, one never quite gets used to the idea of people wanting to shoot you for your wallet, and for all that I've seen on the evening news, Little Rock is just Miami without a suntan. So I packed my 9mm pistol in the carry bag I take with me on most of my trips.

I did my seminar, fortunately without incident, and returned home Friday. Sunday morning I grabbed my carryall, never considering the gun therein, and left for Little Rock Airport. I was flying out to visit a friend in Salt Lake City.

I arrived ahead of time Sunday morning; the flight was on schedule. So far so good. I checked in at the counter and walked to the correct gate. Shoving my bag into the X-ray machine, I strolled through the metal detection frame. It was about that point when things began to take a decidedly downhill turn. The two girls watching the monitor went bug-eyed as a constipated Pekingese, suddenly staring at the screen like they'd just found a finger in their Hostess Twinkie. They glanced at me, looked at each other, then their eyes ricocheted back to the monitor. I was still standing there without a clue.

One girl nervously sidled over to the counter and began frantically pressing something underneath the desktop. Hmmmm... At first I thought she was storing her chewing gum for later. What did I care? But boy, it sure seemed like she was really into getting that gum attached to the desk! The other girl was already backing up so she could get a running start in case I yelled "Viva Castro!" and pulled a grenade out of my armpit.

About this time several things began to happen. My bag came through the machine, and with a sudden incandescence I finally realized what was going on. But before I could slap myself in the head and say, "stupid, stupid," the cavalry arrived from several different directions.

As they surrounded me, one officer stepped forward and asked the inevitable question. "Whatcha got in the bag, fella?"

"Well, a gun," I said, launching into a high-pitched, hasty explanation that they were only partly interested in as they carried me and my bag, quite separately, to "the little room."

The long and the short of it is, they asked me a bunch of questions, then they ran me and my pistol through the computer. Finally satisfied I wasn't a guest star of Unsolved Mysteries or America's Most Wanted, they let me go--without, of course, the pistol. I thought that was the end of it. Hmmmm....

About a month later I get a letter from the Federal Aviation Administration. In essence, it says, "You're in deep muckety-muck. But not to worry, 'cause we're here to help you. You have committed a violation that carries a $10,000.00 fine. Send us a detailed explanation of the whole incident, along with a complete record of any and all crimes you have committed in your entire life. Be sure to include every one, even those you got away with, and maybe we can get this straightened out." Hmmmm....

Okay, so I send them this clever little letter with a complete explanation and an amusing Reader's Digest version of my life, explaining that the only time I had ever been arrested was for sneaking into a drive-in movie, locked in the trunk of a car, when I was a teenager. My friends were nervous--they broke the key off in the lock trying to get me out. It was a sweltering August night. Three hours later, when the police finally got me out of the trunk, I was glad to be arrested.

Well, two weeks later I get another letter. Hmmmm... It says, "We read your explanation, and we don't think you're as cute as you do. We've decided that you're not dangerous enough to be jailed, but you certainly screwed up enough to be fined. Please send civil penalty in the amount of $500.00."

Now I'm reading this, feeling my ankles sinking into the muckety-muck, when down at the bottom of the page the last paragraph reads, "You can contest the matter, but if you do, we're going to go after you for the whole ball of wax--10K, and who knows, maybe a federally-funded vacation. Or, you can take advantage of our special thirty-day offer: plead no contest and pay only half the civil penalty immediately--that's right, only half the retail fine--$250.00, and we'll forget the whole thing."

Now I don't know about you, but the whole thing seems like a cross between a shakedown and a late night TV advertisement to me. I'm waiting for them to throw in a free set of Ginsu knives if I get my money in the mail today.

So I wrote them back, saying, "Just $250.00, huh? Does this deal come with any kind of guarantee?"

Two weeks later I get another letter. It says basically, "We guarantee this is your last chance."

I sent them the $250.00. I'm looking forward to having this whole thing over, and getting my Ginsu knives.

****

THE MARKETING OF CHRISTMAS

Dec. 22, 1988

Ah, it's Christmas again. The smell of fresh-cut Scotch pines fills the air. Bright lights decorate bough and building, and the sound of cash registers singing and card chargers ringing, can be heard well above the jingling of most sleigh bells.

Once again this year, the spirit of Christmas will edge out rationality, and most of us will go cheerfully into debt for an army of friends, neighbors, nephews, cousins, brothers, sisters, parents, office parties, charities, and business associates. This doesn't include the airplane tickets, rental cars, forests of wrapping paper, and the mountains of hams, yams and pumpkin pies destined to undo our diets and raise our cholesterol to a flashpoint.

The one thing that Christmas and the IRS have in common, is that the majority of the country works until April just to pay them off.

Now, before you begin to think I'm sounding like the Grinch, let me say that I love Christmas. I probably appreciated it more when I was a child, and wasn't aware of the mechanics involved, but I still enjoy the holidays and the spirit of good will that seems to pervade the land for a few short days at the end of each year.

I do, however, have a bit of a problem with all the commercial hoopla on this holiest of holidays. It seems to me that there's way too much emphasis on clothes, toys, and colognes, and not enough thought given to the man whose brief stop on this spinning ball of dirt and water made all this possible.

If it makes you happy, go ahead and spend your money like a drunken sailor. After all, it's you who has to pay it back. But sometime during this holiday, take a few moments, whether it be driving in the car with your children, or sitting at the Christmas dinner table, to be reminded and to remind those around you, that this season is not predicated on the price nor the quantity of gifts received or given, but rather that it is a celebration of the birth of Earth's most precious soul.

And stuff a piece of the good cheer that you now carry, into your pocket. Remind yourself occasionally of its presence, and sometime during the year, when times are tough, and things are less than perfect, take it out and share it with those you love.

Merry Christmas, Son

****

SPITBALL

June 1, 1989

I came back from the lake last Saturday afternoon, tired and a little sunburned. Bonnie didn't have anything planned, so I stretched out on the couch and turned on the television. There was a baseball game on.

I don't usually watch baseball, but I sat there fascinated, not with the game, but with the players. I have never in my life, seen a single group of people spit so much. They are constantly gumming great wads of God-knows-what--chewing gum, tobacco, finger nails.

Those people have spitting down to an art form. There's the between-the-front-teeth-spitters, the out-one-side-of-the-mouth-spitters (or out both sides of the mouth at once if they're really good). There's the slow-drippers-between-the-legs (when they're sitting in the dugout), the chin-dribblers (which is accompanied by the back-handed wipe), and the reflex-spitters, who manage a little spittle every eight to ten seconds no matter what they're doing. I have to wonder what matrimonial joys these guys must be off the field. Do their wives keep spittoons strategically placed all over their million dollar homes? And a fancy little spittoon for the Mercedes?

I watched players with such copious wads of Wrigley's and Red Man's best crammed in their cheeks that they looked like chipmunks wearing ballcaps. Once, the game had to be halted while the umpire performed the Heimlich maneuver on a player whose golf ball-sized wad of chaw lodged in his throat as he slid over home plate. I've come to believe that cleats might not have been designed for traction, but rather to keep the players feet off the gooey mess on the dugout floor. I'm convinced that some of those daring slides are nothing more than runners slipping on infielder spit.

After watching a few minutes of the game, it was apparent that another favorite dugout pastime is nose-picking, which is often combined with spitting. Sometimes the reflex-spitters couldn't get their fingers out of their noses quickly enough and they spit on their hands. But it didn't seem to phase them. They just wiped it on their pants with everything else.

I found that nose-picking wasn't simply limited to the dugout. Every once in a while, a devious cameraman would catch an outfielder with a finger thrust to the second knuckle in his nasal cavity, blissfully pursuing an errant booger (usually trying to spit around his wrist and watch the game at the same time). I think it's very possible baseball gloves were originally made as large as they are to discourage nose-picking.

Indiscriminate scratching is another characteristic unique to baseball. Whether it be in the dugout or standing on first base for all the world to see, those guys scratch like a pack of baboons. I kept waiting for them to start picking the fleas off each other in the dugout. Aside from the scratching, phlegm-flinging and nose-picking (which, incidentally, makes snacking while watching a baseball game very difficult), I was amazed at how many of America's heroes, rich beyond their dreams, looked like homeless people in uniforms. Unkempt hair, like straw from Oz's scarecrow, sprouted out from underneath caps, and scraggly, two and three day beards earmarked many a player. They appeared like color-coordinated ruffians, with poorer hygiene than a colony of spider monkeys. And each of them is making more money that the average brain surgeon.

Having spent an evening with baseball's finest, I'm not surprised the great American pastime is struggling for popularity.

****

DROUGHTS AND RAIN

Aug. 29, 1989

Last week I figured if it got any hotter, Polk County was going to win second runner up to hell.

About the time the devil was buying property in Cove, it finally rained. This drought, and the rain that broke it, have given me new perspective. I've lived all over the world, but I had never experienced a drought before--a tree-killing, grass-burning, creek-squelching drought that leaves a person sweating and listless, and searching the afternoon sky for a darkened cloud.

After a while, it takes on character, becomes nearly tangible, almost personal. I watched some of the trees on my property begin to die. The creek dried, the stones in the bed turning dusty and hot. The grass in our yard surrendered to the heat and faded to yellow, my garden struggled valiantly to survive, and I began to hate this torrid creature that held my land in its grip. I could only imagine what the farmers of Texas and Oklahoma must have been feeling.

I was sitting in the den Sunday afternoon, locked into a good book, when I heard your mother calling from the front porch. It was raining.

I stood on the porch staring at the mottled clouds and willing the rain to earth, offering small supplications that it might last an hour. The trees bent to the wind, the rain came down in sheets and puddled on a grateful land and I found myself rejoicing like a farmer in *The Grapes of Wrath*. It was a strange experience for a Caribbean boy. They say that life is a continuous process of learning, and you don't really know something until you've felt it. I believe that's true.

In the baggage of this lifetime, I have now packed away an understanding of drought, and a deeper appreciation for rain.

It is a bittersweet experience, for there is both good and bad in it, but I accept the lesson gratefully.

****

SOMETHING FOR NOTHING

Nov. 15, 1989

It seems like some aspect of the American farming industry is always in crisis. The process continually repeats itself, only the commodity changes. Well, it seems this year, it's the hog farmers.

In a nation where people still go hungry and welfare is still dished out like hot soup at a street kitchen, the farmers of America oftentimes can't afford to feed their own because, of all things, the country has too much food.

If you think that's convoluted try this: At that point, the government steps in and starts paying farmers not to raise things. There are people in this nation who make a living not raising everything from wheat to cattle. This process has been going on longer than you would think. I found the following letter recently reprinted in the Enid, Oklahoma, *News and Eagle*, dated 1940, addressed to Congressman Edgar F. Foreman of Odessa, Texas:

Dear Sir:

My friend over in Terrebonne Parish received a $1,000 check from the government this year for not raising hogs. So I am going into the not-raising-hogs business next year.

What I want to know is, in your opinion, what is the best kind of farm not to raise hogs on, and the best kind of hogs not to raise? I would prefer not to raise Razorbacks, but if that is not a good breed not to raise, I will just as gladly not raise Berkshires or Durocs.

My friend is real excited about the future of his business. He has been raising hogs for more than 20 years and the best he ever made was $400, until this year, when he got $1,000 for not raising about 50 hogs. If my friend got $1,000 for not raising his hogs, would I get $2,000 if I don't raise 100 hogs? That seems logical to me. I plan to operate on a small scale at first, holding myself down to about 400 hogs, which means I should have $8,000 coming in from the government.

Now, another thing: These hogs I will not raise will not eat 100,000 bushels of corn. I understand that you also pay farmers for not raising corn. So will you pay me anything for not raising 100,000 bushels of corn to not feed my hogs I am not raising? I want to get started as soon as possible as this seems a good time of the year for not raising hogs.

One more thing: Can I raise 10 or 12 hogs on the side while I'm in the not-raising-hogs business--just enough to get a few sides of bacon to eat?

    Very truly yours,

      J.B. Lee Jr.

    Potential hog raiser

****

HENRY THE TURKEY

March 30, 1990

Bonnie and I set out to buy a fireplace the other day, and ended up buying a turkey. It's an interesting story.

We drove to Ink to look at a free-standing fireplace a fellow had for sale. Just as we arrived at his farm, our right front tire went flat. While we were changing the tire, a big tom turkey came waddling over, drumming and clicking.

The most difficult thing about changing the tire was keeping the turkey out of the way. He kept rubbing up against me, and trying to crawl into my lap, wanting me to pet him. He and Bonnie became immediate friends while she scratched him and he fluffed up, cooing contentedly.

"He's a bit of a pest," the guy said. "He was raised with puppies and he thinks he's a dog. He's a real unusual turkey and if Thanksgiving wasn't coming up, we probably wouldn't eat him."

I saw the look on Bonnie's face and I knew what was coming. We didn't like the fireplace. It wasn't what we were looking for. But we ended up spending $20 on a turkey--a really amazing turkey.

He growled a little when I picked him up and put him in the back of the pickup, but he was as gentle as a lamb. When we got him home, it became more interesting. I couldn't go anywhere that day without Henry (Bonnie said he looked like a Henry) following me.

Things got more exciting when we introduced him to Mac, our Rottweiler, and Buddy, our Sheltie mix. Henry quickly established a "pecking order," chasing Mac and Buddy around the yard until they both sought the protection of the front porch. Actually, Mac seems to be enjoying a little good-natured competition, but Buddy is absolutely terrified by this beaked demon we've brought into his peaceful little world. Henry growls just like a dog, and fetches sticks well, but he hasn't got his bark down yet. It still sounds like a choked gobble. He loves to be petted behind where his ears should be, and if you sit down, he crawls up into your lap like a Chihuahua. It's pretty weird.

In the last day or so, Henry's finally eased up a bit on his new buddies. Now, instead of the dogs accompanying me to the pond in the evenings and sitting on the dock, it's the dogs, the turkey, and me. I'll admit though, the dock gets a little crowded with everyone vying for attention.

Three months later—

You may remember me telling you about Henry the turkey--thought I'd give you an amusing follow-up.

Henry's now part of the family, and he does indeed think he's a dog. He and Mac chase the car out of the driveway every morning as I go to work, biting (or pecking) at the tires, and Henry, along with our two dogs, dashes out and greets me at the gate when I get home. He has grown quite a bit since we bought him. Actually, he's grown a lot--I can't remember seeing a turkey this big. Henry discovered he had a taste for the pellets I feed my pond catfish--the commercial kind that says, "Guaranteed to add a half-pound of weight for every pound consumed." I've been giving him some every day, when I go out to feed the catfish. I don't know about the fish, but that stuff is sure working on Henry. He looks like a giant beach ball with feathers.

Bonnie and Henry have become inseparable. Where she goes, he goes. We have to leave the door open at night so Henry can see her in the living room or he starts gobbling frightfully. Bonnie's convinced the poor guy is lonely--that he needs a mate, and I think she's right. If she leaves a small garbage bag or a bleach bottle on the lawn, anything that remotely resembles a bird, Henry's on it in a heartbeat. He dances around it fluffing up and cooing, then jumps on it with a vengeance. It's obvious though, that none of this is very satisfying for him. After all, a bleach bottle just lays there...

He gobbles pleadingly at darn near everything that passes by the house-- cats, armadillos--the squirrels would rather deal with Mac anytime. I'm sure if Henry could catch one of our crows on the ground, that bird would be in serious trouble. He's even taken to following Buddy around, which is making the little guy purely uncomfortable.

We don't want another turkey (and we really don't want a whole bunch of turkeys, which I'm convinced, is what Henry has in mind). Bonnie came up with the idea of just studding him out. I'll admit he's a terrific specimen-- smart, loyal, a good guard bird, and starting to rival my Rottweiler in size-- but I'm not sure there's much market for stud turkeys.

Two months later--

Henry, our sex-starved turkey, had gotten so desperate for love he began to pluck out his own plumage--some sort of feathered Freudian self-flagellation thing, the vet told us. Before he pecked himself bald and began to look like Daffy Duck after the bomb went off, we decided to try and find him a mate.

We placed an ad in the paper. "Single turkey, non-smoker, likes long, early morning walks in the yard, seeking serious relationship with same."

A nice lady from out near Lake Wilhelmina called and offered to give us a hen, but after talking to her, we realized she was much better equipped to take care of Henry than we were. She had wonderful facilities, other birds for Henry to associate with, and, of course, a lady bird. It was a difficult choice, particularly for Bonnie, but her affection for the bird was so great, she chose to give him the best shot possible at a good life.

When we got Henry to his new home, and out of the truck, the hen started calling to him. Good ol' desperate Henry perked up immediately and began his Jurassic Park gait toward the pens. When he got his first look at her, I swear his eyes lit up and his tongue fell out of his beak like something in a Wily Coyote cartoon.

We had to help him into the pen--he was a little shy at first--but when she winked at him, that was it. Without going into graphic detail, it's safe to say that those two hit it off almost immediately--no flowers, no candy, very little conversation. The only problem was, Henry had been raised with dogs and had never seen a female turkey in his life. He knew what he wanted--Lord, he didn't suffer from lack of enthusiasm--he was just a little loose on the mechanics of the whole thing. Henry had been practicing on garbage bags and empty bleach bottles at the house, but this svelte little feathered darlin' stirred his passions to the point of short-circuiting what little intelligence can be credited to a turkey. (Although that sounds like a fairly common characteristic with the male gender straight across the board.) For a while there, it looked like a few pages out of the Turkey Kama Sutra.

Finally, thanks to the infinite patience of the female (which is also not uncommon), Henry got it all figured out. Afterwards, he lay back in the pen, looking for a cigarette. She flew up to the roost to straighten her feathers after being somewhat abused by her clumsy mate. We were a little embarrassed for him. We left quietly.

This weekend, we returned to say hello and see how Henry was doing. In a word, I'd have to say great. We were talking with his new keepers at their house, when Henry heard Bonnie's voice. He was a good 75 yards away, over by the pens, but he let out a gobble and started out at a run through the tall grass that separated us. It wasn't long and he was rubbing against Bonnie like a lonely cat while she hugged him.

We miss him at the homestead--his crazy antics and his genuine affection for us both, but we know he's safe and he's fulfilled where he is now.

Sometimes, if you really love something, you have to be able to let it go in order to keep it.

****

NEW WORLD DISORDER

June 30, 1990

Every once in a while, I have to make a trip to a big city somewhere--generally for a doctor's appointment.

I read the paper there, and look around as I traverse the boulevards and side streets--trapped in the metropolitan congestion, overwhelmed by the sheer numbers, appalled at the indifference shared by the inhabitants, and threatened by the capricious violence that lies darkly in wait at any turn--and I'm more aware than ever, that the world outside the small bastion where I live, has shifted on its axis.

When I watch the evening news, it seems as if there is some sort of infectious insanity that, like a virus, has crept across this country and affected its people. There no longer seems to be a clear understanding of right or wrong. Standards of conduct that have guided this nation for centuries have been eroded into ineffectual dogma. John Wayne is gone--replaced by Michael Jordan, Hulk Hogan and Madonna.

Our politicians ignore ethics and integrity and run the country with the reckless abandon of third world dictators. And in truth, we may well be headed toward that status, because the difference between third world and first world is not simply money, but attitude--the relationship between leaders and populace.

In the school yards of our nation, all the emphasis is placed on physical dexterity. Sports programs dwarf academic effort. Those who strive to achieve scholastically are chided, derided, and harassed. I was recently told by a teacher that the emphasis in inner city schools is no longer on education, but on staying alive another day--for students and instructors. What an incredible statement about our society.

The combination of disparate races, cultures, and creeds in this country no longer represents a melting pot, but rather a confused and tumultuous tapestry of peoples--all seeking racial and social autonomy. The foundation on which this nation was built--the innate desire of the immigrant to become an American, first and foremost--has been lost in the shuffle.

It's all pretty scary, I know. I've told you about the disease, and now you're waiting for me to explain the cure, but like a doctor facing a patient stricken with cancer, I come up empty-handed. I think we are destined to run our course, like so many nations before us. (Rome comes to mind immediately.) We have failed to study our history, so we're destined to repeat it. *C'est la vie.*

A friend of mine once told me, "Look at today's younger generation, and you will see tomorrow's world." If you spent a couple days in a Los Angeles mall, that thought would scare the bejeegees out of you.

The "me generation" has be come the "strictly me generation"--the "I'm the one, 'cause I got a gun" bunch.

There is, of course, a part of me that says I shouldn't be too hard on society's latest offering. After all, it was my generation that brought you Howard Stern, crack cocaine, and the Viet Nam War.

Hopefully, there will be a handful of youngsters in this next cycle that'll move to the forefront and pull the fat out of the fire for the rest of them. And I wouldn't be at all surprised if most of America's new leaders are born from its heartland--places where integrity and responsibility are still common--places like this little town of ours.

MAKING BUCKS FROM BUCKS

Sept. 4, 1990

The other day I went to the doctor for my annual physical, a debasing ritual of nakedness, poking, prodding and coughing that I could gladly do without. It does, however, lend perspective to one's overall health; so each year about this time I grit my teeth and do it.

Slumped in a plastic chair in the reception room I picked up a copy of some Arkansas outdoor magazine, and while paging through it I came across an advertisement in the "New Products" section that set me to giggling maniacally.

The product was called Supreme Buck Urine. Yep, that's right, Supreme Buck Urine. Not regular stuff, this, but high test twaddle for the wholesale attraction of deer of all kinds, or perhaps for the hunter who wants a really rugged cologne. I've heard of a lot of strange sales businesses, from marketing bottled tap water to Florida swampland, but I think this might top them all. I mean, for goodness sake, these people are making a living selling...urine!

The ad went on to mention that Supreme Buck Urine is collected at the company's state-of-the-art collection facilities. (I'm not making this up, I swear.) Now that got my curiosity piqued. How exactly is state-of-the-art buck urine collection done? Is there a very quiet guy in a camouflage suit and a measuring cup hiding in the woods, discreetly following deer around until that special moment? He'd have to get awfully close, and have a very steady hand.

Well, I took the number at the bottom of the page and called the company that afternoon. I had a couple of, what I thought, were legitimate questions. A girl answered on the third ring. I told her I wanted some info on her urine. She said, "Excuse me?"

"You know, Supreme Buck Urine?"

"Oh yeah, that."

I said I wanted to know the inside scoop on buck urine collection. And what about rutting versus non-rutting buck urine as mentioned in the ad; I mean, was a rutting buck more, or less cooperative? I struggled to make the conversation a straight transaction, but try as I might I couldn't keep the smile out of my voice. Pretty soon we were both giggling. Finally we were laughing so much she said I'd have to call back, maybe talk to the boss about the technical side of buck urine collection. I said, "Okay, who do I ask for?"

She said, "Buck."

I said, "You gotta be kidding!"

Seems Buck was out doing some collecting and field testing, whatever that means. I suppose you can use your imagination.

****

COFFEE ANYONE?

Jan. 4, 1991

There's hardly an outdoorsman, or woman, who doesn't enjoy coffee. Those early summer sunrises on the lake and those crisp, cool, fall mornings gathered around the breakfast campfire are almost always accompanied by a cup of steaming coffee. We may have said goodnight to the moon with a bottle of Old Jack in our hands, but come morning, it's that cup of java that brings us back to life.

That's the good side of coffee, but I have a suspicion that there could very well be a darker side to the amber liquid.

Although most of the big coffee companies don't like it advertised, coffee contains the most widely consumed, habit-forming drug on this planet--caffeine. Compton's Encyclopedia defines caffeine as a "mildly habituating" (tell that to a six cups a day drinker) drug belonging to the xanthine family, a central nervous system stimulant most prevalent in coffee.

The fact is, a lot of people don't do well on coffee, it produces side effects from mild jitters to outright hostility in many people. I think there's a lot of people out there who drink coffee that shouldn't. There may be whole groups of people, perhaps even nations who shouldn't be drinking coffee at all. It could be that coffee consumption has a subtle, long-term negative effect on most societies. I did a little research on the history of coffee, and the locations and progression of global aggression correlated with the cultivation and the consumption of coffee. It makes for interesting reading.

The use of coffee originated in the Middle East somewhere around the sixth century AD. The Arabs have been drinking coffee the longest. Now there's a nice peaceful group of people for you. They haven't been able to establish a treaty among themselves or with their neighbors for over 2,000 years. This is a race of folks who are fond of tying bombs to themselves and running screaming into groups of other people they don't care for. How many cups of coffee do you suppose those guys consume before an act like that? More than one espresso I bet.

Coffee was brought to the Americas (Martinique Island in the Caribbean, to be exact) in the mid-1600s by one Captain Gabriel Mathieu de Clieu of France. Europe had already discovered its fondness for caffeine. The Spanish were young coffee junkies when they began the pillage of Central and South America and the genocide of the Aztecs and Incas. Before that, they blended blind religious fervor with steaming java and came up with The Inquisition.

Things quieted down for a hundred years or so in the 1700s, as coffee got a foothold in the islands and cultivation began to spread into South America. Columbia, Venezuela and Mexico were sleepy little countries south of the border until the mid-1800s when major cultivation and consumption of coffee began. All of a sudden there were revolutions popping up right and left. Complacent peasants in serapes and sombreros were suddenly gathered together in angry mobs, brandishing machetes and muskets, and dragging local officials to the closest wall for target practice. That's not to say that they didn't have cause. But what was the catalyst for all their newly developed indignation? Could it have had something to do with the tons of coffee they had recently begun to grow and drink?

The African nations have never been known for their stability, but in

past centuries they reserved the majority of their mayhem for each other.
The introduction of coffee production in the early 1900s may have been the
straw that broke the camel's back. Shortly after coffee production began in
earnest, we saw the development of the Mau Maus, a wide-spread group of
independent thinkers who felt any interaction with white settlers and their
families should be accomplished with a machete. The intensity of inter-tribal
warfare with Africans has escalated in recent years to a profound new level,
causing millions of deaths and turning residents of entire countries into
refugees. But oftentimes nowadays, as ABC's cameras scan the bulging
refugee camps in Zaire or Botswana, you'll see that nation's guardians
swigging down coffee. Kind of makes you wonder, doesn't it?

Here at home, things are no better. Coffee consumption in the United
States in the last 30 years has shattered all previous records. In the interim,
the very fabric of our society seems to have been rent. We have been treated
to random sniper attacks, drive-by shootings and burgeoning violence in
every imaginable fashion. Domestic abuse is epidemic. Hardly a day passes
that a lone gunman somewhere doesn't get so ticked off that he just has to
shoot a half-dozen people. Maybe if he'd have just passed on that last cup
of coffee....

On the other hand, societies that have been known for their order and
their social and cultural decorum, such as Britain, China and Japan, avoid
the use of coffee. Curious, isn't it?

These are just observations, and I'm not implying an unequivocal
correlation here. It could all just be coincidence, or motivated by changes in
the infrastructure of society and the population explosion. Me, I'm not going
to worry about it. I'm just going to wrap up this letter and get it to the mail
box, 'cause it's time for a coffee break.

BIG CATS AND BOONES FARM WINE

June 14, 1991

This sweltering summer weather may not be good for anything but staying in the shade and sipping something cool, but it is the time of the year when we see some of the largest catfish being taken from our waters here in the Midwest.

Having read a recent story about a monster 100-pound plus catfish being caught in Missouri, I was reminded of some of the tales I'd heard of "the big boys,"--"the ones that got away," here in area waters. The stories of giant catfish in the Mississippi and Arkansas rivers go way back, to the 1800s. There were probably even larger cats in those waters then than there are now, but my theory is that a few of those old 200 or maybe even 300 pound leviathans still exist. They are the ones that create the "great catfish tales."

I heard of a fellow fishing the Arkansas River who threw out a gaff hook baited with a whole chicken, tied to his anchor line, while he fished for bass. He claimed the fish that took that chicken picked up the anchor and carried him and his bass boat 10 miles downstream before bending the gaff hook straight. They say he only fishes from the bank nowadays.

One of my favorite stories was told to me by an area sheriff, about a group of Galveston hippies camping out on the Arkansas River in the 1970s. They stumbled into his office early one morning telling a story of a giant marine creature (there were various descriptions, depending on how glassy-eyed the witnesses were) that sucked their van into the river in the night.

Evidently, sometime during the course of their stay, they decided they wanted to catch a big catfish, so someone tied a large hook to a nylon rope, baited it with a pound of summer sausage and threw it out into the water, tying the other end to the bumper of the bus.   It seems the Volkswagen bus was parked on somewhat of an incline near the water. After an evening of "Puff the Magic Dragon" and "Where have all the Flowers Gone?" complimented by several strange-smelling cigarettes and a bottle or two of Boones Farm wine, the group crawled into the van and passed out, visions of Woodstock dancing in their heads.

According to the more lucid witnesses, their sleep was anything but peaceful. They had no sooner settled down than the van began to groan, sliding inexorably toward the water's edge. Those who could, stumbled out into the night to find the nylon cord at the back of the bus taut as a tightrope, the other end weaving back and fourth downstream as some monstrous water-creature struggled with a mouthful of summer sausage and a shark hook. They claimed the emergency brake gave way and the creature towed the van right into the water with all their camping supplies. (Not to mention a half-pound of pot and a case of Boones Farm, which was discovered the next day when the van was salvaged from about 10 feet of water.)

It could have been the emergency brake was never on, or was kicked off by a restless foot that night. But those folks never changed their story, and the shark hook was found straightened like an arrow. I know some of this may sound like research for a fresh water denizen book ("Maws" maybe?), but it's really not the case.

I guess what I'm saying is, the uncertainty of a subject makes it exciting. One of these days we may see someone actually land one of the old monsters out there, and prove that they still exist.

Until then, you better be careful where you dangle your toes.

****

LOOK OUT, THE PHONE'S RINGING

Oct. 27, 1991

I suppose it doesn't matter whether you live in the hills of Arkansas or in a beach bungalow in L.A. If you've got a phone, you automatically fall prey to the dreaded telephone solicitor, that friendly fellow with the artificial attitude who won't take no for an answer, who's certain he has a service or an item that you just can't live without.

It's two o'clock on Sunday afternoon. I've raked the leaves in the front yard and cut a cord of wood for the cold front they say is coming in. Bonnie's done the breakfast dishes and straightened up inside while I showered. It's an unseasonably pleasant day; a cool breeze is coming through the open windows. Seems like a great time for a nap, or whatever. We sidle into the bedroom, kick off our slippers and snuggle up, but we no sooner get the covers pulled over our heads when the phone rings.

I struggle out of bed with a groan and grab the receiver. "Hello."

"Hello, is this Jake, Jake Strider?" says a disgustingly congenial voice that could only belong to a salesman.

A part of me wants to say, "No, no this is not Jake, unfortunately he died yesterday--got run over by the tractor and the hogs ate him." But I don't.

"Yes?"

"Jake, I'm Gerald from *Time/Life Books*. Jake, how are you doing today, Sir?" (There's that generous use of my first name, followed with a question about the weather or my health. It's a salesman for sure.)

Now I feel the urge to contradict the initial acknowledgment of my name. (Excuse me, did I say I was Jake? No, no, I'm sorry. I'm Fred, his cousin. Jake moved to Argentina yesterday, doing research on the Mabuto tree frog--endangered species, you know. He probably won't be back for a year or two.) But I don't.

"Fine, I'm fine. What can I do for you?"

At that point Gerald launches into a spiel on the deal he has for me today: all these magazines he can get for me at only one-third the cover price. I've been picked out special, 'cause I've got great credit and I'm a wonderful person and this deal wouldn't even be possible if it wasn't for a survey they were conducting on what people read. You know--intelligent people like me. I'm beginning to feel like I'm knee deep in muckety-muck, wishing I was back in bed with the covers pulled over my head. I decide to get out of this, tastefully, artfully.

"Excuse me. Gerald, wasn't it?"

"Yes, Jake?"

"Gerald, did I mention to you that I'm blind? Yep, blind as a bat. I'm so blind my seeing eye dog needs a seeing eye dog. I couldn't even tell you where the magazine rack is, let alone read something from it." I smile; I'm sure I've got him. But Gerald is hard core.

There's a pause. "Does your wife read, Jake? This would make a great gift for her. In fact, I'm certain you would want her to have such a wonderful opportunity." I have to think fast.

"Yes, I would get it for her, if she was still around."

"Still around?" Gerald says cautiously, sensing a trap.

"Yeah, sad to say, she's gone--abducted by aliens about a week ago."

"You mean like spaceships and blinking lights?" I can hear the incredulousness in Gerald's voice.

"No, kidnaped by two Latinos in a '65 Chevy, and she hasn't been heard from since."

Gerald senses that he's losing, but he's tough. He's a closer if I've ever heard one. No more ploys now, no more Mr. Nice Guy, Gerald goes in for the kill, one more shot.

"You got a dog or a cat?"

"Yeah, both. Why?"

"Let me tell you, Mr. Strider (not Jake, I noticed) I don't think there's much in these magazines worth reading anyway, but the paper has really great absorption qualities. I mean, if you've got a puppy, or a cat with the squirts, you can pull out the pages and spread them on the floor. Works really great; it'll save your rug. Have you got a fireplace? This stuff burns better than dry tinder--" At this point I resort to my final tactic.

Reaching for the cordless electric shaver that I leave by the phone for occasions such as this, I turn it on and run it across the mouthpiece of the receiver while shouting in the background, "Hello? Hello? Are you still there? Hello? Damned line's gong out again!" After about 15 seconds, I notice the line's gone dead. Gerald realized he had met his match.

Now, I know I could have just told Gerald to kiss my posterior and hung up, but he gets that all the time. This way, being beaten at his own game, will eat at him for weeks--might even cause him to quit his job. Then there'll be one less solicitor to bother me on Sunday afternoon.

****

THE TRAIL OF TEARS

Dec. 6, 1991

The other night I watched a documentary hosted by none other than Kevin Costner, of *Dances With Wolves* fame. It was about the manifest destiny of America's pioneers--the westward migration of those tenacious souls who crossed the new frontier. It presented an enlightening look at the lands, the people they conquered, and the nations they dispossessed in the process.

I am proud of my heritage, as most Americans are, but watching that film I found myself strangely sad and slightly ashamed.

I'm certain that the noble savage was, in some instances, not quite as noble as we are led to believe, for they were human and perfection is not a characteristic of this creature, man. Yet watching that show and listening to their words, there seemed to be a quality of integrity, a guilelessness and a love of the earth, and yes, a nobility that far transcended what virtues could be found in those who had subdued them.

In an age where we are so critical of atrocities of any sort, so haughty and so quick to condemn, we should occasionally be reminded of our own transgressions, so that we do not repeat them. To that end, I would share a poem with you. It is called

"Somewhere on the Trail of Tears...."

Hey na hey Great Spirit, sing our song of passing and open wide your arms, for I am coming home.

They took our lands and sent us away with promises. They placed our feet upon a bitter path and pointed towards the setting sun, and we went. Even though the small voices inside us cried, "No, this is wrong..." But we trusted. We did not understand, or we refused to see, the width and the depth of the white man's guile and greed.

For of all the things the white man did, he promised best of all.

Hey na hey Great Spirit, set my feet upon the path. Take me past the sorrow, to the village of my father.

So it was that we began the journey of a nation. Four thousand souls who traded their freedom and their future for a handful of empty pledges. And when the white man's words changed like the seasons and his summer promises turned to winter lies, we looked at each other and cried, "What have we done?" But our feet were on the trail and there was no turning back. You cannot change the color of the moon nor the course of the sun for the wanting of it.

So on we pressed, to camp that cold night, somewhere on the Trail of Tears....

Hey na hey Great Spirit, light a sweetwood fire to warm the lodge, for I am coming home.

When there was no more food in our bellies, we dreamt of the full fields we had left and we starved. When the winter wind ate at our skin and we stumbled in cold despair across the flat, hard plains, we dreamt of the warm hills of home and our tears froze on our cheeks. And when there was no more room in our bodies for pain and no more hope in our hearts to sustain our spirits, we died, somewhere on the Trail of Tears....

Hey na hey Great Spirit, lay back my buffalo robes for the long sleep, for I am coming home.

One bitterly cold night, as I slept beneath a wagon with my child in my arms, I dreamt. I saw my husband and me riding through the warm summer meadows of dandelion and marigold, past peaceful stands of birch and cedar, painted in the colors of the season.

I could feel my child move, contented, in my belly. I felt the caress of the sun on my hair and shoulders as it gilded the leaves of the trees around us. My husband smiled and held his hand out, and I reached for it... But I awoke then, holding only my child's death-cold body in my arms, for her spirit had passed in the night, somewhere on the Trail of Tears....

Hey na hey Great Spirit, light the trail for our loved ones to the happy hunting ground, for they are coming home.

New moon followed old as we plodded on in silent desperation, adversity chasing us like winter wolves, bringing down the frail and the weak. And when hope had turned to ashes and faith had faded like the waning sun, when there was no more blood in the body of this nation, the great Cherokee heart stopped and the spirit fled, somewhere on the Trail of Tears....

Hey na hey Great Spirit, make them remember. Let our passing not have been in vain, to the everlasting shame of those who sent us, and the everlasting sorrow of those remained. For now, I too, am coming home.

****

THE GREAT CATFISH BAIT FIASCO

April 30, 1992

I heard a funny story the other day, relating to catfish baits and the manufacture thereof. I thought I might pass it along, providing a chuckle and a warning.

There are numerous catfish baits on the market, and many of them are produced with formulas that are closely guarded secrets. One of the most popular, Sam's Never Miss, made in Oklahoma, has been catching catfish for over 30 years, with the ingredients known only to the owner, Naomi Hardin. One of the trade secrets in the catfish bait business is the method used to combine a number of noxious, organic ingredients and keep them from eventually emitting sufficient gas to produce an explosion in a sealed container.

The truth of the matter is, most people don't know this.

Billy Bob Baker and his cousin, Shep, a couple of Arklahoma border boys, definitely didn't know this when they decided they were going into the catfish bait business. Now, Billy and Shep weren't terribly bright souls to begin with, which is one of the reasons they chose catfish bait making as opposed to brain surgery. Their research into ingredients consisted of taking the lid of two or three existing brands and sniffing them. With a solid formula in mind then, they began to combine cheese, cow blood, dough, and other miscellaneous spooky ingredients into a thick, sticky paste in a 20 gallon wash tub. They had purchased six dozen half-quart jars with screw lids at a garage sale. Into these went their "Catfish Delight!" formula. Shep screwed the lids down tight, slapped a label on them, and they were in business. They loaded all 72 jars in the back of their '81 Cordoba station wagon and headed off to make their fortune.

It was a hot summer morning....

The plan was to hit every bait store between Poteau and Little Rock. When they ran out of product they'd head home and whip up some more. Morning stretched into afternoon, and the temperature began to hover in the mid-90s. By the time they reached Mena, the jars in the back of the wagon were reaching critical mass. Billy and Shep were, of course, blissfully unaware as they headed south, through town and into the hilly section of Iron Mountain outside Potter.

They had just reached the crest of one of the larger hills when the first of the jars went. The explosion set off a chain reaction, and in seconds jars were exploding like microwave popcorn, slinging shattered glass and catfish bait everywhere. The reeking station wagon was careening down the hill at breakneck speed, jagging and weaving like a cattle-prodded cat. Billy screamed as he was slapped in the back of the head by a wad of catfish delight, and accidentally jerked the car into the path of an oncoming truck. Jars were bursting so fast that the inside of the Cordoba looked like a food fight at a high school cafeteria. Shep, covered with bait goo and bleeding in half a dozen places from glass shards, shrieked at the approaching truck and jerked the wheel back the other way, which was both good and bad.

The overcompensation pulled them out of the path of the truck, but sent them hurtling off the road as the next hill began its incline. They sailed through the air like an extreme sports auto daredevil team, screeching like baboons, covered with Catfish Delight, bracing themselves for the impact. As fate would have it, the vehicle soared over an adjacent fence and landed squarely in the center of a small pond just off the highway--a catfish pond....

When those catfish caught scent of the boys and their vehicle, well, it was like feeding time at the zoo. Shep, who lost an earlobe, said that they were lucky to escape with their lives, that the catfish darn nearly ate the seats out of the station wagon. Billy Bob and Shep left their car to the catfish, and gave up on the bait business. I heard they got into making rubber worms, which they figured was a safer enterprise.

I suppose the moral of this story is combustible catfish bait is never going to be a big seller, or maybe stinking and driving don't mix.

****

HONESTY

July 1, 1992

We live in an area where I truly believe honesty and integrity are still considered valuable commodities. There are many places where people feel that what they can get from a given situation matters more than who they are.

But honesty, like most things, atrophies if not exercised. A friend of mine and I were talking about the value of character the other day and I was reminded that integrity is much like virginity--it's usually given away, not taken, and once it's gone, it's real tough to get back.

Little white lies are the ultimate villains in the loss of honesty. They erode the bastion of integrity in each of us. We lie generally because we don't want to face the consequences or accept the responsibility of our actions. The truth is, if you're willing to admit a mistake--Okay, I did it. It was stupid of me, and I'm sorry--you steal your accuser's thunder. You leave them no ammunition. Contriteness is a wonderful weapon in the arsenal of the honest. Besides, if you lie, you have to remember what you supposedly did or didn't do, or what you said. Lord, as if life wasn't complicated enough.

Here's a little story on honesty I remember from my younger days:

When I was in college, a professor of mine began a discussion on integrity, but the bell rang before he could complete it. There was a long weekend coming up. As the class put papers away and began to rise, he said, "To better understand honesty, I want each of you to go to the library and read the first five pages of Hemingway's 44th chapter in *For Whom The Bell Tolls* over the weekend.

The following Monday, as we settled into our seats, he asked, "Who read the assigned pages in the 44th chapter of *For Whom the Bell Tolls*?" There was a show of hands.

The professor smiled. "That particular book contains only 43 chapters," he said. "Now, I'll complete my lecture on honesty."

****

DO CONGRESSMEN REALLY HAVE PLOOP FOR BRAINS

Nov. 28, 1992

The other day I came across and article in a local magazine that really got my hackles up.

The Federal Government, notorious for mismanagement of funds, has declared, for lack of monies, it is closing eleven fish hatcheries in the Southeastern U.S. this coming year. Fifteen more are scheduled for closing, but they have yet to be selected.

Although none of the initial eleven are in Arkansas, there is great concern by the Arkansas Fish and Game Commission, as well as local citizenry, that one or more of the hatcheries in our state are earmarked for extinction. I don't know about you, but this just plain ticks me off.

Fishing is as innate to Arkansas as its mountains and its pines, and as much a part of our outdoor traditions as hunting the deer and the turkey of our heartland. Even more importantly, it is an essential part of our children's heritage. Yet if our government, with its screwed up sense of priorities has its way, this may begin to change within a few short years.

The whole thing made me so mad I was compelled to do a little research. I've told you what the government doesn't have the money to support. (This is the same government you pay all those taxes to each year.) Now let me tell you what they are funding with your dollars.

First, let's talk big money, then we'll get into a couple smaller absurdities.

#1. This year alone we spent 226 million dollars on the Federal Bilingual Education Act, so we could teach immigrant children attending U.S. schools in their own languages, rather than have them learn English. That sure makes good sense....

#2. How about this: Last year 67,000 drug addicts and alcoholics collected over 350 million dollars in "Supplemental Security Income." What's that? Well, it's a nifty little piece of legislation that says drug and alcohol addiction qualifies as a disability that keeps people from working. (I'll bet it does!) So they are entitled to monthly social security benefits. Okay, let me make sure I've got this right. All I have to do is get hooked on drugs, and the government will pay me a minimum of $5,000.00 a year. That makes good sense. I guess you could call it the "Getting High With A Little Help From My Friends" program.

I promised you a couple of lesser priced federal spending absurdities, and I won't let you down. These are real zingers.

The Environmental Protection Agency gave the state of Utah almost a million dollars this year, to fit cows with special plastic devices gauging bovine flatulence and its effect on global warming. Now, I gotta ask you, have our congressmen gone mad, or do they just have cowpies for brains? I mean, they just spent the equivalent of the combined yearly federal tax payment of an average Arkansas township so that someone could bungee strap baggies on the butts of a bunch of cows and measure how much methane is expelled when a heifer passes gas.

I know you're thinking that last one is going to be hard to top, but my last example deals with the Federal Grants Program, which I'm certain is staffed exclusively by lobotomy patients.

I had a friend who owned a construction company in Little Rock. Two of his employees, young college graduates, had studied the Federal Grant procedure extensively in their last year of school. They were determined not only to take advantage of it, but to demonstrate the inanity of the system.

Following federal guidelines, they applied for a grant. They filled out all the forms in triplicate, sent in the required letters of recommendation and qualifications, then waited patiently. One day several months later they showed up for work all chuckles and smiles, and gave their notice. Their $300,000.00 grant had been approved--they were off to Alaska to do a comprehensive study on the internal temperature of hibernating Brown Bears. Yes, $300,000.00 (a good portion of which I'm sure was spent on Alaskan girls and Yukon Jack whiskey) for taking the temperature of sleeping bruins.

Now, you've got to figure they ain't gonna get that thermometer under the bear's tongue, so that leaves only one other port of entry, and as challenging an enterprise as that might be, I can't see the results being worth a third of a million of our tax dollars. Yet some pointy-headed bureaucrat with more responsibility than brains decided it was a worthy endeavor.

These are some fine examples of what they're doing with our tax money.

They are closing National Parks and federally funded state fisheries, diminishing our most precious heritage, the outdoors, while they fund projects ranging from the sublime to the ridiculous--projects that rend the fabric of this society rather than mend it. It isn't right. It isn't even American, and it won't change--in fact it'll get worse--unless we do something about it.

Write the Governor, call your congressmen, tar and feather a liberal bureaucrat.

****

MY POND

March, 22, 1993

Late last summer I had a pond built on our property. No sooner had the last blade of dirt been deposited on the dam than the record drought of '92 began. For months your mother described my pond as the front pasture moon crater, and when finally, a little water was deposited in it, it became known as the African mud hole.

Finally the drought broke with the great flood of '93, which washed away houses, roads, and bridges throughout the county. The good news was, my pond filled nicely. The bad news was, it leaked, which I'm told is common with new ponds. The information made it no easier to deal with the condition. But even with the leaking, it has held enough water to be called a respectable pond.

Last fall, I stocked it with fathead minnows, crawdads, and a few fish--catfish and bream--to begin my ecosystem. This week I added a few more catfish to it, and next month I will begin stocking a handful of bass, to entertain me in the evenings after work. It's just a hole in the ground with water in it. A small dock protrudes into the edge of the pond--a display of optimism, taunting the receding water to rise around it. Nonetheless, I love it.

It's hard to imagine how much satisfaction I have received from this shallow body of slightly turbid water. It's such a treat to sit on my dock and watch the evening sky paint itself on the surface of my pond. Van Gogh would be left in envy at its artistry. Bugs skitter nervously across the placid mirror. Bream and minnows rise, brushing lines and circles on the surface, and tiny wind demons preceding each rush of breeze carve exotic patterns on the canvas nature has painted, and I am quietly enveloped by the magic of it all.

Finally, doves make their last flight across the liquid sky before roosting, the encroaching shadows erase the original art work, and I'm left with darkening water and the stillness of evening. But if I'm willing to wait long enough, the canvas changes to stars and moon, and the occasional pale wisp of a passing cloud.

My daily rendezvous with nature (weather permitting) provides me a rare sense of peace and equilibrium. It gives satisfaction independent of ego--a wonderful experience.

This year, I'll plant some willows around the western edge, to add to the daytime landscape and enhance the evening *art nouveau*. By late summer, my bass will be fat and happy, and we'll tease each other from opposite ends of a monofilament line. They, along with those feisty bluegills, will etch bolder, ever-broadening circles on the evening canvas. By then, cicadas, crickets and frogs will add an audio track to mother nature's display.

I can hardly wait....

****

THE ONE THAT DIDN'T GET AWAY

May 10, 1993

Like most rural Americans, I like to fish. I take the sport fairly seriously, using the proper rods, reels and tackle, but beyond that I generally just put the boat in the water, aim it at a likely area and pretty much hope for the best.

I have a friend, however, (I'll call him Jim) who has elevated the sport of fishing to something very near a religion. He has tackle boxes that would rival Hillary Clinton's luggage. Lures? Let me tell you about lures. If it resembles anything that might fit in a bass's mouth, he's got one. If someone tied a hook on a doorknob and advertised it on late night TV as the latest Crappie Killer, Jim would have one the next day.

Like any number of religions, he has costumes and rituals that go with it. He's got trout fly hats, BASS jackets, and belt buckles the size of dinner plates with life-like reliefs of fish that look like they're jumping out of his bellybutton.

He spits on his bait before casting. He sprays all sorts of noxious scents on lure and bait, odors only a fish or a starving raccoon could appreciate.

He even kisses his lures, but generally not after spraying them. His wife broke him of that habit. She told him, "You can kiss your lures, you can kiss me, but if you spray them lures with that #@%@ and kiss 'em, your only chance of gettin' lucky relates strictly to fishin'."

Jim looks at this fishing thing as a contest of intelligence between him and the fish. He's one of my closest friends, but he's not one of my brightest friends and for all the accessories, ceremony and effort, the fish sometimes win. This can throw him into a depression that makes Barbara Streisand's bad moods look like tea time with Shirley Temple.

As for myself, if I have a particularly bad day of fishing and need to boost my spirits, I have one little ritual. I take the stringer of big bass I caught two years ago out of the freezer I let them thaw out enough to get the frost off, and I shoot an instant picture of me holding them up and smiling. Then I send it to one of my old fishing buddies with a note saying, "Boy, what a day! You should have been here!" Works every time.

This brings to mind a particular fishing trip that my friend Jim and I took to Bull Shoals Lake, just above the community of Mountain Home. Actually it was our last fishing trip together. Come to think of it, I haven't heard much from him since then. I'll explain....

It's a great lake, Bull Shoals. It has thousands of acres of clean water, lots of dead trees around the shore for crappie and bass cover, big catfish and stripers in the middle and good trout fishing.

We eased the boat into the water a half-hour after dawn. Pale white shrouds of mist still blanketed the lake. The soft swirls of early morning feeders could be seen on the surface around us. A big bass whorled the water next to the boat, sucking down a luckless insect. It was the kind of scene that both warms your heart and gives you a mild case of the hangover shakes as you try to thread the eye of your lure.

Jim was bait casting; I was fly fishing that day. I'm not a great fly fisherman, and I think that's where the trouble began.

About midway into the morning, I drew back my rod for a cast, the line and the fly floating effortlessly over us. The line straightened perfectly behind me, but just as I came forward with the rod, my attention was caught by a beaver surfacing next to the boat. The line and the fly tracked slightly sideways. About that time two things happened: Jim set his rod down and stood up to stretch, and my fly whizzed by, solidly snagging him in the earlobe. He let out a yelp like a salt-rocked coon dog, flailed with both hands and took a step to turn. I think that was his first mistake. Stepping on his tackle box, he lost his balance, and in less time than it takes a lizard to snatch a gnat, Jim was headed for the water.

He went in headfirst and came up gasping and splashing, eyes the size of saucers, water spitting out his mouth like one of those fountains in Hot Springs. My first thought was, "There goes the fishing in this area." My second, as I watched him begin to flounder and gurgle, was that Jim doesn't swim real well.

In his panic, he had turned away from the boat. I figured I better redirect his attention, so tightening my line, I gave the top of the rod a little pop. Jim screamed like a pubescent schoolgirl, grabbed for his ear and my firmly attached fly, and grasped the line.

He was a big one, I knew I was going to have to play him. I loosened my drag and let him run a little, giving him some line as he splashed with one hand in an awkward circle. But if he started to sink or get too far from the boat, I gave him a short tug and immediately got his attention again. Finally, after one of the best fights I could remember in recent fishing history, I got him close enough to the boat to consider landing him. Problem was, he was too big for my net and I didn't bring the gaff. Besides, though grateful to be boat-side, Jim had a look in his eyes that said he was less than pleased with me. So, in the end, I elected to tow him the short distance to shore with the electric motor.

As he crawled out of the water like early man and blew his cookies on the grass, making sounds like a cat hacking up a rat, I was pretty sure fishing was over for the day. I was right. After removing the fly from his ear, Jim didn't speak to me all the way home. I haven't heard much from the ungrateful cuss since.

In closing, just remember, if you head out to your favorite lake and catch a bunch of big ones, take 'em home and freeze 'em, stringer and all, 'cause you never can tell when you're going to have a bad day fishing.

****

TICKS AND FLICKS

June 14,1993

Bonnie and I, and the dogs, took a couple of hours off yesterday afternoon to take a stroll through the pasture and along the woods at the northern end of the property.

It was a glorious spring day, rich with the colors and smells of a reborn earth, and even though the underbrush was thicker than I had expected, we really enjoyed ourselves. It wasn't until your mom and I had arrived home that we realized we had acquired a number of unwanted guests on the sojourn. Yep, you guessed it, ticks, the bane of the bush, nemesis of the woodsman.

Accompanying them was the vanguard of this season's chiggers. Now there's another of Mother Nature's most miserable creatures.

I've said before, that chiggers were like Arkansas's Yeti or Sasquatch: everybody talks about them but nobody's quite sure what they look like, and one encounter with them is generally enough to satisfy a person's curiosity.

That night as I plucked ticks from various parts of my body, I was reminded of a movie I had seen years ago, about a backwoods area besieged by giant ticks that had somehow mutated after being exposed to the TCH (Tetrahydroide Cannabinol) of some wild-eyed marijuana grower's crop in the countryside. The movie was a very low budget, CTS-rated (crummy to stupid). In fact it was so bad, if you put your hat on backwards and drank a six-pack of beer quickly, it became pretty good. I think it was called *High Tick Country* (not referring to altitude).

The ticks in the flick looked like grapefruits with legs, and whole flocks (herds? bevies? whatever you call a bunch of ticks) slurped the blood from unsuspecting country folk with the sounds of someone enjoying the last of their milkshake. The solution to those whacked-out arachnids was nowhere near a tweezers and a Dixie Cup of alcohol. It was more like a solid swipe with a Louisville Slugger #32.

I've digressed. I apologize. The point I was making before I got sidetracked, was that these critters are a real nuisance to the outdoorsman. There are, however, a few preliminary precautions you can take before heading out on that hiking, hunting or fishing trip that can make the day more enjoyable and less itchy.

First off, rubber bands placed tightly around the base of your pants legs will help discourage access to the more delicate parts of your anatomy. I was told that in the old days, folks smeared coal oil on their wrists and ankles, around their cuffs, before they went out to pick blackberries. I don't recommend it though, unless you're using disposable clothes, and you're not planning on spending any time with your mate for the next couple of days. A healthy dose of conventional sprays such as "Off" or "Cutter" on the legs, arms, and across the back, are a good deterrent, but those sprays do have a tendency to bother some people's lungs.

One of the best topical preventatives was given to me by a Realtor friend who shows a lot of rural property. It's a product sold by Avon, called Skin-So-Soft. She said that she had tried everything, but the Skin-So-Soft worked much better for her, without the respiratory problems.

A word of caution to you men, however, It will make you smell so good that I wouldn't recommend it on long camping trips without women.

Once you've got the little buggers, there are some tips to getting rid of them. With ticks, be absolutely certain you get the head of the creature when you pull it off. Otherwise, you're most likely to suffer from itching and infection. A dab of alcohol afterwards is standard procedure.

I was told you're not supposed to disturb the tick greatly before removing it, or it will regurgitate into your skin and cause even more infection. I guess the trick there is to stroke the little fellow gently a couple of times, maybe whisper to him softly, to relax him, then quickly rip his tiny head out of you before he has time to think about it.

For chiggers, the best treatment seems to be a commercial product called ChiggerRid. A smear of tobacco chew from the mouth is supposed to work well also, but I'm not ready to take up chawin' to get rid of the little insects.

What it comes down to is, an ounce of prevention is best with these critters. And if you're wandering through the woods in an area you suspect might have a pot patch or two, carry a Louisville Slugger.

****

THE PRICE OF SPORTS ENTERTAINMENT

Nov.1, 1998

I rarely read the larger state or national newspapers. They depress me too badly. The ceaseless flagellation this poor country is receiving from self-serving politicians, me-first, special-interest groups, and indignant, hyphenated Americans leaves me wanting a prozac and a cigarette.

I used to find some respite in the sports pages, but not any more. I can't, for the life of me, understand what has happened to the sports industry in America. How did we come to these strangest of times, when a man can bite off another man's ear and get paid $27 million for it. Truly, we must be in the last days of Rome.

Let's get past the ear-gnashing for a moment. How in the name of sweet-eared corn have we come to the determination that beating the pulp out of someone for about 15 minutes is worth more than the combined yearly salaries of the top three heart surgeons in the United States?

We've got people creating financial dynasties in this country who couldn't manage a job as a stock boy in Wal-Mart. There are those regally rich souls who, without their almost idiot-savant talent of throwing a ball through a hoop, or crashing through a defensive line, would be behind a counter somewhere, saying, "Do you want fries with that?"

The irony of the whole thing is, there isn't one of these athletes that wouldn't take a 50 percent slash in pay this very moment to keep their job, the alternative being a commonplace occupation--working as a mailman, or a convenience store clerk (which, in many cases, would find them under-qualified).

Worst of all, these ill-mannered egotists have become America's heroes. Our children (and many of their parents) put their hats on backwards, stare glassy-eyed at the idiot box and cheer each on-court tirade.

"The Duke" would be turning over in his grave.

The outrageous salaries and the sky-rocketing cost of attending sporting events show no signs of abating. The enthusiasm of blindly rabid fans, living as vicariously as any good Roman in the Colosseum, still bolsters support for a greedy sports infrastructure. The only chance for change will come when the sports lawyers, promoters and the club owners allow their avarice to get the better of their intelligence, and the price of a ball game ticket and a hot dog escalates past the working man's weekly salary. Then the whole thing may collapse like a house of cards.

On the other hand, a dyed-in-the-wool Laker fan might not consider a week's salary that bad....

****

BUCK RODEO

Nov. 21, 1994

Recently, a friend of mine and I were discussing the calibers of various deer rifles--their trajectories, range, and knock-down power. During our conversation, my buddy related a funny story which made his point about the importance of stopping power (and accurate shooting) regardless of what you're hunting.

An acquaintance of his, Fred, was hunting deer on Rich Mountain one season, using a weapon of questionable stopping power. I could give you the caliber, but as soon as I do, you'll tell me you've hunted water buffalo with the same weapon and never had a problem.

Anyway, he was returning to his pickup after a luckless day when he spotted a large, eight-point buck less than 50 yards from the highway. Without hesitating he raised his gun, sighted and fired. The animal bolted a dozen feet, then dropped. When Fred reached the deer, there was an impressive wound and it appeared lifeless, so he decided to gut it on the spot. He put his gun against a tree and drew his knife, then came up behind the animal and straddled it, grabbing the horns and drawing the neck back to bleed it. But as he did, the animal suddenly lurched to it's feet. Now, I think it bears mentioning here that Fred was not a big fellow. He probably wouldn't have weighed 120 pounds fully clothed and sopping wet. The deer, on the other hand, would have hit nearly 200 pounds.

The deer rose up like Lazarus and bolted down the hill, Fred astraddle its back, clutching its antlers like a wide-eyed reluctant rodeoer. Don't ask me why he didn't jump off, or fall off, but he didn't. At the same time, Fred's warbling shrieks didn't do anything to soothe the panicked buck, which was racing for all he was worth through the woods, careening down the hill toward the highway.

The last of the buck's strength gave out as it reached the road. It stumbled and finally collapsed on the centerline, sending Fred sprawling next to it, one hand grasping the antlers and the other still holding his knife. Battered by low-hanging branches and lacerated by pine cones and needles, ol' Freddy looked like he'd just lost a fight with a Veg-a-Matic.

He had no sooner thudded to the pavement when he heard the screech of tires. Fred closed his eyes and braced himself for the impact. A moment later, when he realized he hadn't been hit, he rolled over and found himself staring at the grill of a 1988 Cadillac Coupe DeVille. Doors opened and an elderly man and his wife came around to stare at the hunter and his deer.

The old man shook his head and said, "I'll admit it's a wee bit impressive, but from where I'm standin', son, it don't look like you're havin' all that much fun. Why don't you just buy yourself a gun, and shoot 'em, like everybody else?"

****

ONLY FOOLS PLAY NAKED PAINTBALL

Jan. 30, 1995

The other day I ran into Roger, my hunting buddy from Mount Ida, and, as usual, he had a story to tell me.

It seems that he took up the sport of paint ball recently: simulated war games played in the woods, with weapons that shoot paint pellets. It's an adult version of "capture the flag" but the airguns used in the contest push a paintball out at better than 300 feet per second, and when you get smacked by one of those balls, it's enough to make you holler like a salt-rocked beagle. The first time you play, you feel like Rambo, decked out in cammos, weapon in hand, too smart to get hit, bulletproof... But by the end of the first game, after the more seasoned players have shot the bejeegees out of you, a sense of caution starts to edge out raw courage.

Like Roger says, "Only a masochist plays careless paintball." Now, Roger is an ex-Vietnam vintage woodsman, and figured that he would be a natural for the game. He would have been, but there were a couple of unfortunate twists his first time out.

It was a clear, remarkably warm, fall morning when the two teams gathered at the field for a manly contest of "grab the flag and shoot the snot out of your neighbor." The players dispersed and the game began. Roger immediately separated from the others on his team, having formulated an idea for an ambush. Sneaking deftly though the woods, he chose a halfway spot that appeared to be a likely approach for the enemy. Quickly, he removed his army entrenching tool and dug a shallow grave-like hole. He slid into the trench and covered himself with leaves and a little dirt, propping his head up just enough to give him a view of the trail in front of him. His cammo gear, face-paint and weapon blended into the flora, making him nearly invisible. He smiled. It was just a matter of time....

Unfortunately the best laid plans of mice and men often go awry. Roger was waiting patiently when, off to his right, he heard something, a scratching sound. At the periphery of his vision the lower bushes were moving--Roger lay dead still, not wanting to turn his head for fear of giving away his position. The enemy was approaching!

As he listened to the advance of his opponents, he thought it strange that there were no harsh whispers, no heavy breathing. They were moving very lightly for soldiers.

About that time the family of skunks came tramping out of the foliage-- a mother and three young, foraging in the mulch and leaves. Roger tensed for a bolt, but decided against giving up his position. Maybe they would just work around him. Unfortunately, the skunks made a bee-line for the freshly dug soil that Roger had spread over himself. He lay perfectly still as the four varmints crawled around and over him, sniffing, scratching and digging.

He might have held out had it not been for the mother skunk's persistent clawing as she tried to unearth the candy bar she had discovered in his jeans pocket. When she was only a layer of denim away from shredding delicate flesh, his resolve dissolved, and with a yell he bolted upright, tossing startled skunks in all directions. The frightened skunks threw their tails in the air and did what frightened skunks do, pretty much all over Roger.

Now, there's very few of you country folk out there who don't know how purely nose-wilting a close-up encounter with an angry skunk can be. Roger found himself sprayed from head to foot. He smelled so bad his beard was curling and it hurt to breathe. My phewed friend couldn't stand it. He ripped his clothes off, stripping down to his skivvies, grabbed his gun and barreled out of there like a cross-country racer at a nudist camp. Dashing though the woods like a man possessed, the naked paintballer ran smack-dab into an ambush set up by the other team.

Roger was pretty well hyped as it was, but when those paintballs started smacking tender flesh, he set a new record for the nude broad jump and never looked back. Still, they managed to hit him with so many paintballs that when he got to the parked cars, someone remarked that he looked like a bad Picasso painting.

To add insult to injury, he smelled so terrible that they made him ride on the luggage rack of the Jeep all the way home.

I can just imagine what that must have been like, with the golf-ball-size welts, the paint, and the smell. But Roger, with his indomitable spirit, says he plans to try it again.

The things we men will do for a little outdoor fun.

****

PISCES ANGLUS NECESSITUS

April 28, 1995

Your mom can't understand how I can enjoy fishing in some of the well-stocked, small, farm ponds in the area. She says it's like shooting fish in a rain barrel.

"You know you're going to catch fish when you go there," she says. "It doesn't offer the challenge of a big lake."

Not being a big fisherman herself, she's missing the most salient point regarding this particular endeavor. I like the challenge and the uncertainty of big lake fishing, but I'm addicted to the swirl and the tug. I'm a full-fledged victim of the widespread disorder called angling fever (oftentimes used with an explicative in front of the word, as in %$#@$ angling, or commonly, #%* %#@&@ fishing, by wives and girlfriends of those who suffer from the disease).

I can't help it. I have to feel that sudden stop of the line on retrieve, the arch of the rod, hear the sweet squeal of the drag at least once a week, or I begin to get irritable, suffer from night sweats, and get hives on my forehead. When my affliction starts to get the better of me (usually about midweek, Wednesday or Thursday afternoon), I'll sneak off to one of my neighbor's ponds and treat the symptoms of my disease, for there is no cure once you've become infected with the *Pisces Anglus Necessitus* virus.

Not only do we poor, suffering souls spend wads of cash on vast amounts of equipment and clearly bizarre-looking lures, we are willing to go to nearly any length in our pursuit of this finny panacea. People backpack into inhospitable terrain braving mountainous inclines and temperature declines just to flick a fly toward a small, scaly mouth. They paddle down steaming, mosquito-infested jungle rivers teaming with creatures that would gladly reverse the intended process should the fisherman become careless, all for a cast at some exotic set of fins.

Some fail to return from their wilderness sojourns, but the ones that do, tell wild tales of lures bitten in half, sizzling, drag-melting runs and fifteen-yard tail walks, and the disease spreads....

To those of you not yet afflicted with this malady, I say beware. Don't let them fool you with enticing ads in glossy magazines. This is not a sport, it's a sweet addiction, a pleasuring infection. To all those out there with loved ones who suffer with *Pisces Anglus Necessitus*, I say give them their time to treat the illness, and pity them, for they are nearly helpless in their struggle.

****

FACING DEATH HEAD-ON

Dec. 14, 1995

I was headed down Highway 8 East the other day, when there, on the side of the road, I noticed a raccoon. He was dead as dirt, upside-down, legs sticking up and stiff as a board. He'd obviously been looking right when he should have been looking left. As sad as it was for me to see one of God's creatures having met his fate, I couldn't keep a small smile from the corners of my mouth, for it reminded me of my very first trip through Arkansas. Seems like a 100 years ago. Most of all, the sight of the raccoon was a particular and poignant reminder of the fellow I had been traveling with, Loony Tony Lamar. I can hardly see a legs-up animal on the side of the road, or smell peach brandy and not think of that guy. Now, I know you must think that's a pretty strange combination, but I can explain.

Loony Tony (who came by his name honestly) and I were returning from Wichita, Kansas, where I'd just bought another giant portable BBQ machine for a catering business I owned in South Florida for a while. Tony worked for me, on and off (mostly off), for about two years. If the fish weren't biting and the dogs weren't racing, or if the weather got too cold for the beach, he'd probably show up; otherwise, it was a roll of the dice. But when he did show, he was a hard worker and good company. Tony was also an excellent cross country driver, which was why he was with me that afternoon as we traveled East on Highway 40, headed for Little Rock.

We were driving straight through to Fort Lauderdale in five-hour shifts, stopping just long enough to fuel, feed ourselves and use the restroom. It was my turn to drive, so at our last stop Tony picked himself up a pint of his favorite, Morton's Peach Brandy.

We got to laughing and telling stories, and Tony began nipping seriously at that bottle. Pretty soon it was empty, and he was high as a kite, crazy as a road lizard. I was thinking maybe we should find some coffee when all of a sudden he yelled, "Stop! Stop the car!"--his hands waving wildly as he pointed at something ahead, to the side of the road, a psychedelic gleam in his eye. It was a Monday afternoon; there was little or no traffic. I slammed on the brakes and swerved off the road, screeching to a halt.

There in front of us was the biggest raccoon I'd ever seen. I mean, this son-of-a-gun must have weighed in at seventy pounds. He was as dead as last week's news, on his back, legs straight out, and rigid as a fur-covered card table. Before the truck even stopped moving, Tony was out the door, yelling something about dignity and death, headed for the animal.

Sitting in the truck, I couldn't believe what I was seeing. Loony Tony had grabbed the giant raccoon, turned him over and stood him up, facing the oncoming traffic. Tony stepped back, admiring his work, and I found myself smiling, then laughing. Suddenly we were both laughing our fool heads off, and finally I understood. What was a painful last grimace had been turned into a defiant snarl as the raccoon proudly faced his nemesis'--man and the automobile. He had been given a modicum of dignity in death, stubbornly standing there as if to say, "Come on sucka', give me your best shot!" (And I'm quite sure someone did, not long after we left.) Nonetheless, it was still rewarding to see Rocky Raccoon staring onward as we drove away, a fairly empty pint of peach brandy at his side.

We were feeling so good, I let Tony buy another bottle of Morton's best, and we stood up animals for the next 200 miles. Why, we managed a little dignity for three armadillos, two 'possums, four raccoons, and a Chihuahua before we cleared Louisiana.

I guess the point I'm trying to make here was best put by Tony the next day when he had sobered up. He said most everyone he knew, including himself for the longest time, was afraid of dying. We seem to perceive it as some dark, confusing affair. Somewhere along the line he realized that if you take something less seriously, it can't frighten you--that dying should be viewed with less fear and trepidation and more a simple acceptance of what it is: the final, essential part of life.

Now, I'm not saying we should take this final communion with the

Great One lightly, and I'm not saying that when Grandma kicks the bucket you should stand her up on the highway. (That would freak out the tourists, wouldn't it?) But I have often wondered, at somber funerals marked with dark clothes and hushed tones, whether the one who had just passed into that bright realm would really have wanted everyone acting that way.

For me, I think I'd like to go out with a little dignity and a little levity, like a nice coffin and a Groucho Marx mask.

Y'all watch out for those raccoons, hear?

****

ACORNS AND HUNGRY BASS

Feb. 11, 1996

Largemouth bass are one of the most voracious and territorial gamefish in North America. In part, it's these qualities that make them so sought-after by anglers. A hungry bass, or a spawning bass, will hit just about anything that gets near it, from bottle caps to butterflies, which is probably why today's fishermen are bombarded with such a wild assortment of lures.

Helicopter baits, noise-making lures, floating, diving, suspended, fur-covered, natural colored and now, even autographed lures adorn the shelves of every respectable tackle store. (Has the modern bass become that discerning?)

The remarkable thing is that most of them seem to work to some degree, simply because of the rapacious nature of the fish. I once caught a three pound bass that had nearly a pound duck in its gullet. The bird was so big, the feet were sticking out the fish's mouth, yet he still struck my Hula Popper. Talk about attitude.

That reminds me of a story about a friend of mine who was having a problem with squirrels disappearing on his place.

We were sitting on my buddy's porch, looking out at the little lake that bordered his property. At the shoreline, there were several big Oaks whose branches stretched out over the water. Occasionally you could hear an acorn fall from a tree and slap the still surface of the lake. Squirrels chattered and ran back and forth along the bank scavenging nuts for the winter to come. Right at the water's edge, in front of the house, was an old, partially submerged stump. My friend pointed to the stump.

"Take a good look at that," he said. "You see what's laying on top of it?" I squinted out against the glare of the afternoon sun. There on the flat surface of the weathering wood sat a plump, shiny acorn.

"Just watch that for a little while," he said, with a knowing smile. No more than five minutes had passed when a curious squirrel leaped from the bank to the stump. The little rodent stuffed the acorn into his mouth and turned to leave, but he had no sooner reached the edge of the old tree when suddenly, a huge bass burst out of the water and snatched the creature right off its perch. There was a moment of furious splashing, then all was silent, the ripples fading into the bank.

"That was the most remarkable thing I've ever seen!" I exclaimed, turning to my friend."

"That wasn't nothin'," he replied. "The really amazing part is watchin' that darn bass spit the acorn back onto the stump."

THE IDIOT BOX

Oct. 3, 1998

Late fall is a glorious time of year here, but the days are growing shorter and I can already sense the change in the air that heralds the inevitability of winter.

This means more hours indoors, some of which, I hate to admit, will be spent in brainless enterprise, staring at the flickering tube which has become the primary recreation, educator, trend-setter, opinion-maker, baby-sitter and curator of the absurd for the general populace. Having recently spent a little time watching television, my opinion of it hasn't improved. On the contrary.

There's an expression regarding probability ratios that goes something like this: If you gave 100 monkeys (each) a computer keyboard to hammer on, at some point in time, the odds are that one would produce a great literary work. I think the executives of the major TV affiliates apply this same philosophy with their writers. In fact, I think they may have advanced this concept one step further; their writers may actually be monkeys.

The network executives seem to adhere to the idea that if a little is good, then a lot is better when it comes to the type of programs they air. For months, even years at a time, the public is bombarded, beaten into boredom, by the same style or type of show. The formula for the last couple of seasons has been cop shows and hospital shows. Lord, I'm so tired of seeing people shot and mended I could scream.

These episodes about bullets and bandages have been interspersed with dreadful sitcoms about pods of dysfunctional people who live together in apartment buildings. Most are so poor that even their canned laughter sounds forced.

The current rage for the Mutts and Jeffs of TV programming is sensational/informational broadcasting--the Geraldo Rivera syndrome--*The Inquirer* gone television. To name a few, there is *20/20, Dateline, 60 Minutes, Prime Time, Coast to Coast, Turning Point, 48 Hours,* and *48 Hours After.* (I'm not kidding about that one.)

I'm up to my little brown eyeballs with tiny, malformed babies in hospitals, reformed drug addicts and unreformed drug addicts, people who think they've seen aliens and people who claim to be aliens (from Mars and Mexico), and information on enough strange diseases to make me feel purely uncomfortable just shaking hands with anyone.

The informationals are surrounded by intellectually stimulating episodes of *The Adventures of Hercules, Xena, the Warrior Princess*, and *Roar*-- sword and sorcery flings that would make Conan turn over in his grave. These shows are like live cartoons featuring very politically correct casts of races that didn't co-exist in the time frames and geographic locations in which they're shown. If it wasn't for the push-up bras of the heroines, the shows would be absolutely intolerable.

It's bad enough that we're left with such poor choices, but adding insult to injury are the dozens of commercials they squeeze into each hour. I've often wondered how many commercials the viewers will allow before they say enough is enough. We're very near the half commercial, half program mark now. Maybe 2/3 to 1/3 or maybe even 3/4 to 1/4? Who knows? The people making the shows are the same ones making the commercials. They probably figure if we're dumb enough to watch the slop they're creating, we may well accept an announcement of what was supposed to be on, followed by an hour of commercials telling us what to eat, wear, drive, and drink.

When it gets to the point that I'm spending more time watching advertisements on feminine hygiene and mass-market cheeseburger peddling than the featured entertainment, it's time to bow out with a portion of my self-esteem still intact.

To those of you still glued to the tube, I say, try turning off that one-eyed Cyclops that mesmerizes your family each night, and try talking with each other for a change. Get out a board game and get the whole family involved. Pick up a book and experience a whole new form of entertainment--one that requires you to use your mind to visualize characters and situations. Bore sight a new gun, tie some flies for spring fishing. Get a hobby, get a life.

Get away from something that tells you how the world is and discover how the world is for yourself.

****

DEER CAMP

Oct. 16, 1998

It's nearing hunting season again, and everyone's getting ready for deer camp. There are a lot of reasons people go to deer camp, but having spent some time with a number of those one-week-a-year wilderness aficionados, those male-bonding purveyors of campfire tales and loyal Jack Daniels fans, I think the least of those reasons is to shoot a deer.

I mean no offense. I think the opportunity of spending a week in unfettered camaraderie with mother nature and your best friends is a glorious thing:

The hazy ribbons of early morning mist lacing about the trees as you crawl from your sleeping bag and the crispness of fall morning greets you first hand.

That pungent, sweet smell of an open wood fire, and the unparalleled aroma of bacon and eggs cooked in a black camp skillet.

The smell and the taste of coffee as you cradle the cup in both hands and ward off the morning's frost.

The heavy, incredibly satisfying feeling of a weapon in your hands as you traipse through the riotous colors of a fall forest.

The swift, sharp chill that sets on the woods when the sun finally dips below the trees and the charcoal gray shadows turn to indigo.

The welcome warmth of the campfire at night, its yellow-red reflection dancing on trunk and bough, providing that innate sense of security and lighting the periphery of the impenetrable darkness surrounding you.

The tales told, and the small truths spoken to one another around that fire which might never have been uttered in the light of day or within the life that exists outside those woods.

The soft rustle of night creatures in the darkness around the camp as you settle into sleep, and the chorus of cricket and frog.

These and many other experiences and sensations provide the motivation for deer campers.

And there's always the chance that you might see a deer.

GETTING SKUNKED

Feb. 22, 1997

5:15 a.m., Friday: It's coal dark and cold outside. I'm tucked in my warm bed, having this wonderful dream I vaguely remember now-- something about catching record size bass in a pretty little pond, with the Dallas Cowboys Cheerleaders cheering me on. I'm smiling....

Suddenly this smell comes wafting into my dream, this incredibly noxious odor. The cheerleaders are holding their noses; the scene is beginning to fade. Poof! It's gone. I'm awake.

The acrid, eye-watering scent is so strong I can almost taste it. It hurts my teeth; my nosehairs are curling! Bonnie rolls over and sits up next to me. "Skunk," she mumbles in the darkness.

About that time I hear Mac, our Rottweiler, come charging around the house and onto the porch, banging on the door, wanting in.

Fat chance, I think to myself, knowing sure as fire who aggravated that skunk. Mac bangs again. I switch on the night-light and stumble out of bed, grabbing a sweatshirt and a pair of pants. Bonnie starts closing windows. The living room smells like somebody spray-painted the air with skunk-whiz. I hit the porch light, open the door a few inches and peer out. I thought the living room reeked, hah. The smell outside that door crams its fingers up my nostrils and jabs the back of my eyeballs, doing permanent damage to my olfactory nerves.

Mac stands balefully at the steps to the porch. He resembles something that might have come out of a Stephen King movie directed by Woody

Allen. He has rolled in the ash-colored, powdery dirt by the workshop in an attempt to alleviate the smell. The only thing that's still black are his eyes. He looks (and smells) like something that's been dead for weeks and dug up.

Foolishly, I step out the door. Mac takes this as a signal that everything's fine, that maybe I want to play, and comes bounding across the deck--140 pounds of smiling, slobbering skunk-stink. Hands out, and yelling at him not to touch me, I stumble backward, hit the low porch rail and tumble head over heels off the deck.

They say timing is everything. The skunk has chosen this same moment to make it's escape from under the house. Hitting the ground with a thump, I see this black and white blur racing out of the shadows at me. I let out a yowl like I've been jabbed with a hot poker. The skunk hisses and jumps-- all four feet in the air like a Pepe le Pew cartoon, and tail up, disappears in another cloud of skunk phew.

6:00 a.m.: The sun has yet to come up. Both Mac and I have banged on the door, trying to get in. Bonnie has opened it just enough to beat us both with the broom, informing us that we're to live in the shed from now on. It is not promising to be a good day.

The upside to this whole affair, if there is one, is that I discovered an excellent formula for neutralizing skunk odor. It was in an article sent to me by a friend in Florida. I tried it later that morning and miraculously, it worked!

I'm going to pass it on, in case you or your animals have a run-in with that testy little, black and white varmint. No, it's not tomato juice, which works only marginally. This formula, I guarantee, will eliminate nearly all traces of odor.

Take one quart of 3% hydrogen peroxide, 1/4 cup of baking soda and one teaspoon of liquid soap. Blend well and soak all affected area, then rinse. That's it. Works like a charm! You may need to multiply the formula several times to cover a large dog, or a person, but it virtually extinguishes the odor--I stress that this concoction does not disguise it, but actually dissolves it chemically.

I must caution you however, that this cannot be bottled or it will explode--something to do with the volatile ingredients.

In closing, I recommend some preventive medicine. Take two cotton balls, spray them with room deodorizer and set them by your nightstand. If your dog gets skunked, and howls and bangs on the door in the middle of the night, stuff one cotton ball up each nostril and go back to sleep.

****

BE CAREFUL, AMERICA

April 2, 1999

I grabbed my cane, called the dogs, and took a stroll to the creek Sunday afternoon. It was a beautiful, unseasonably warm day, and as I walked, I let my mind unspool. I was reminded then, as I ambled through the trees following the stream, that living in the hills here in Western Arkansas, we sometimes forget there's a real world out there, and it's not all that pretty.

The television is our primary link to that outside world. *Nightline, NBC News, Maury,* and *Howard Stern* remind us that it can be ugly out there-- ugly and incredibly stupid. I can watch one of those shows and be "get down on my knees thankful" that I live in a small community in the mountains of the Midwest.

A news announcer recently said if Michael Jordan ran for governor of his home state, he would probably be elected hands down--a man whose one and only skill is throwing a ball through a hoop, could become governor of a sovereign state in this union by simply throwing his hat in the ring. Does that make you un comfortable at all? It should.

Did you know professional wrestler Jesse Ventura was just elected as the governor of Minnesota? Big sports fans, those Minnesotans. I wonder what they'll think when he starts body-slamming senators who don't agree with him. (What if he gets bored with being governor and wants to wrestle on weekends?)

They paid Mike Tyson $26 million Saturday night for displaying his usual crass personality and lack of sportsmanship. What a sterling example for the black youth of America he is. What a message he delivers. The irony is, if he wasn't brutalizing people for a living, the best Tyson could hope for would be a job guarding a junkyard somewhere.

We have sports personalities with the intellect and temperament of wolverines amassing financial dynasties in this country. They are the heroes of the new generation. What a terrifying statement that is.

Over 50 percent of America believes infidelity, grand jury perjury and obstruction of justice by the highest office of the land is really no big thing.

Ninety percent of the people in this country no longer trust politicians. The other 10 percent are politicians.

Our president gave his State of the Union message this Tuesday, as his impeachment trial continued....

Someone once said: Self rule is the privilege of a moral and responsible society. When a society becomes irresponsible, someone will inevitably come along and take that privilege away.

Be careful, America.

****

REFLECTIONS ON LIFE

March 26, 1998

Now that I have reached an age where more of my life is behind me than ahead, I've become slightly introspective. The invincibility of youth has been tempered by experience, not all of which was good, and the result, I like to think, was wisdom. What this really boils down to is, I'm just about smart enough now, to recognize when I'm doing something stupid. I might still bunji-jump off a 50 foot cliff, but at this point, I'd be more inclined to assure myself that the cord attached my ankle didn't measure 60 feet. All this wisdom seems to be just oozing out of me, so I thought I'd pass on a few observations to the younger generation.

First of all, let me tell you how important it is that you cherish the significant happenings of your life. Memories are a lot like fine wine; the older they get the more precious they become. Take the time to make them, and remember them, lest you find, as you grow old, that your glass is half empty, instead of half full.

Make a conscious effort to lock the smells of a spring morning and the colors of a fall sky into your memory. Watch the rising sun turn the ocean to gold, or guild the bright green leaves of an old oak, and intentionally etch that scene in your mind like a snap shot.

While you pursue outdoor endeavors, be reminded to take advantage of the moment, and secure in your recollection the pure sensual enjoyment of what you are experiencing. Don't just go out and fish and hunt. Make a deliberate effort to remember a flight of ducks across a rose-colored sky, and the swirls of feeding fish in the shadows of a lake at sunset. Consciously record your experiences with nature, and teach your children to do the same. These memories will carry you through life. They can be taken out at any time, like a favorite book, and paged through at your leisure. They enrich you as a young person and comfort you as you grow old.

Learn to associate smells, sights and sounds, particularly music, to the times of your life. Consciously relate a song to a time, or a friend, and you will be giving yourself a wonderful gift that you can experience over and over again for as long as you live

Remember the make, model, and color of your first car, and the wonderful times in the front seat, as well as the back.

Take a moment occasionally, to recall the lights of main street on those sticky hot summer nights. Never forget the full name of your first real date.

Most importantly, I say take pictures of the places and the times of your life. Don't find yourself so busy enjoying the experiences that you forget to record them. Fail to do this, and you'll hate yourself years down the road, when your memories have turned to black and white.

Take videos of friends and lovers, wives, and especially your parents, so that you can hear their voices as well. These are the secrets to joyful recollection, the keys to a savings account of memories that pays dividends forever.

Moving on to other valuable information: Life is basically a roll of the dice. You are inevitably going to experience good things and bad things. But never let the prospect of failure or pain prevent you from rolling those dice.

Take a few chances, live a little, use your imagination. Never forget your roots, but remember that there is a huge, inconceivably exciting world out there, and it is your birthright as a human being. You are not required to settle for, nor do you have to accept, that which gratified your father or his father before him.

Embrace only what satisfies your heart, don't be afraid to challenge what doesn't.

For goodness sake, don't let passion ruin your judgment and your life. Be careful out there. Don't find yourself cast into the ranks of those young people with mortally wounded lives, whose uncontrollable libidos overrode their intelligence and chose their future for them. Find out what life is all about before committing yourself to a single individual from which 90 percent of your joy or misery will be derived.

It is both a glorious and dangerous world. There are a multitude of parts and there is some assembly required. How you put it together, and what you end up with, is up to you.

****

WARNING!

June 12, 1998

Put me in a department store and inevitably I will drift toward the sporting goods. I suffer an inexplicable magnetism to rods and reels, shiny lures, and the weighty, satisfying feel of stock and barrel.

Such was the case the other day when your mother and I stopped at our area store to do a little shopping. Knowing that I would disappear at some point and unerringly end up in the outdoors section, she, as usual, took my wallet and my credit cards, gave me back $10, smiled and told me to have a good time.

Feeling like a kid with a dime in a nickel candy store, I was browsing the outdoors isles, examining this and that, when I started to notice how many products in sporting goods have warning labels on them. I began to walk around the rest of the store, trying to determine the variety of items with warnings pasted on them or printed in the instructions.

For the next week, I paid attention to the wonderful world of warning labels wherever I went.

Even for someone who recognizes that we live in an age where people with IQ's smaller than their shoe sizes are becoming wealthy overnight for doing something incalculably stupid then hiring a New York lawyer to make someone pay them for it, I was still amazed.

Basically, I discovered that there are two kinds of warnings. The first, regarding federal offenses, intimidates you, threatening government intervention, fines and prison time. These relate largely to copyrights on books and videos, transportation of flammable liquids in illegal containers, walking through customs with undeclared fruits and vegetables, or glassy-eyed with white powder in your mustache, or shipping bombs, dead animals, or your cousin Hernando through the U.S. Postal Service.

The second, and certainly the more widespread, is basically a disclaimer, saying: If you're mud-dumb enough to put this in your eyes, over your head, rub it on you, eat it, drink it, or put your hand in it while it's running, we're not going to be responsible. Some of the things I found warnings with really epitomized the preposterous state of affairs in which this society finds itself.

In sporting goods, Baitmaster Fish Attractant, which comes in a variety of flavors such as nightcrawler, crawdad, and baitfish, warns you not to spray the contents in your mouth. Are they crazy? One smell of that stuff and you're never going to have to worry about wanting to taste it. The display racks in the catfish bait section are also stacked with attractive-looking pre-packaged doughballs in almost any party flavor--chicken, shrimp, fish, cheese, and clam. There are bait containers that look like squeeze tubes of Kraft cracker cheese, filled with exotic delights such as chicken liver, worm paste, or cheese and blood. They have warning labels as well.

Speaking of catfish baits, I'm reminded of a funny story....

I had a friend who had a habit of keeping his catfish bait in the back of the kitchen refrigerator, to keep it fresh after it was opened. One night, he had a zinger of a party at his place, and when the hors d'oeuvres ran out, a couple of his snockered friends went to the refrigerator looking for more. Before he realized what had happened, they had eaten two tubes of worm paste on saltines and were halfway through their second bag of lip-smacking, clam-flavored doughballs.

They seemed to be enjoying themselves, and he didn't want to ruin the party, so he let them finish the doughballs. I guess if you're drunk enough that you can't read the labels, the smell probably isn't going to bother you.

Sorry about the digression--I'll go on.

The instructions on hair dryers warn you not to use while showering or sleeping. I can see the distinct advantage of not putting a hair dryer in the shower with you, but I don't understand how you can sleep and dry your hair at the same time.

Warnings packed with large vacuum cleaners state concern for use around small pets and birds. I like that one. It conjures up all sorts of amusing images.

All toasters recommend that you do not immerse the product in water while using. I understand that. Common sense tells you that bread and water are not a good combination.

One of my favorites is fast food hot beverage cups that now have labels stating that hot coffee may very well be found in the hot coffee cup. This, of course, is a result of the lady who ordered a cup of coffee from McDonalds, spilled it on herself, then promptly sued the company for $6 million and won, because of all things--the coffee was hot! I wonder what her shoe size was.

One of the saddest things about that incident is, somewhere there's a lawyer who's proud of his part in that judgment.

If this kind of thing keeps up, we may have to replace the old axiom, "The harder I work, the luckier I get," with, "The dumber I be, the richer I am!"

I'm waiting for them to put warnings on hammers, saying, "Attention!

When this device is activated, right hand may damage left hand." Or a warning on table forks, "Not responsible for operator injuries due to spastic nervous conditions."

I suppose we can't really blame the companies who attach these ridiculous labels to their products, what with the legions of people out there perched like vultures over a fresh kill, just looking for an opportunity to take someone to the cleaners. It's become a way of life. A sad, disheartening statement on today's America.

But let's be reminded, every time someone files a suit, you and I pay for a little piece of it in the products that we buy and the insurances that we purchase. Let's do our part to keep statistics down. Remember, if it has blades and whirs, keep your fingers out of it. If its electric, keep it out of the bathtub. If it says, "Not fit for human consumption," don't put it in the refrigerator. If the label says, "Hot," let's try to avoid using the human litmus test method of confirming that. If it says take one a day to feel better, don't take five, hoping to feel great.

Let's all do our part to put class-action attorneys out of business and more money back in our pockets, where it belongs.

****

VISITORS

Nov. 30, 1998

A writer friend of mine dropped by yesterday afternoon. We got into a lively conversation about planet earth and its inhabitants. The next day, he dropped me off a copy of an article he had just sold to oné of the big science fiction magazines. In a few words, it sums up a lot about this species of ours. I thought I'd pass it on to you.

_____

One hundred miles above the earth, just beyond the tug of the planet's gravitational field, a lone spacecraft drifts leisurely along at the speed of light, orbiting the green and blue ball below.

The occupants of the craft stare out of the viewport while seated at the operations console, observing, commenting....

"It appears to be a quiet enough little planet, doesn't it?" said the navigator.

"Looks can fool you," said the communications officer, scratching his ear with the tip of his tail. "I've been receiving their satellite broadcasts-- global and area news reports, and something called HBO. This place makes Gladron II and it's carnivorous plant life look like a galactic vacation spot. In fact, the governing federation has forbidden any power-down landings here."

"Yes, I read a report on the planet recently," said the captain, staring at the spinning globe through bright obsidian eyes. "Seems they are considered one of the most profoundly dangerous life forms in the galaxy-- technologically advanced savages--driven by greed and lust, tortured by jealousy, and spurred to violence by anger. Now they are developing more and keener weapons with which to kill each other--a dangerous combination."

"But a most interesting species, full of strange and curious customs," said the communications officer.

"For instance," asked the navigator, one of his ears perking up.

"Well, even for savages, their myriad religions contain the most startling inconsistencies. They have gods that provide love and forgiveness on one hand, then promise everlasting agony as retribution for the slightest indiscretion on the other. Each philosophy is threatened by the next, and nearly all of them claim to be the only way to the Great One--it's all very confusing.

"Not a day passes on the planet that thousands do not die bludgeoning, shooting, and bombing each other. They not only do this out of rage and greed, but they do it in the name of religion. Can you imagine--they kill each other for their gods," added the communications officer incredulously.

"What is the society's motivating force?" asked the navigator. "Surely there must be something that makes their confusing, pitiful lives worthwhile."

"Yes, apparently there is," replied the captain. "The great motivator for the planet seems to be small, colored strips of paper imprinted with pictures of dead leaders.

"Nearly the entire species toils at all sorts of tasks--they have great structures dedicated to the storage of--and they oftentimes kill each other--

all for these tiny pieces of paper distributed by the governments. Every once in a while, someone makes their own pieces of paper, and the chiefs of the society get very angry."

"Is this a religious phenomena?" asked the navigator.

"Not that I can determine," the captain said. "Though many seem to worship the pieces of paper, and most of their religions require that their followers regularly give many pieces of paper to protect that philosophy's gods, and sometimes, to keep their leaders from being taken by the gods."

"Seems curious enough, but frankly, not very logical," said the navigator. "Does this species provide itself much in the way of entertainment?"

"Oh, by the bright black irises of the Great One, do they have entertainment," said the communications officer. "I have watched their HBO station, which I believe stands for Hypertension, Bloodletting and Orgasms. Half the globe spends hours each day transfixed to tiny screens, watching members of their species perform remarkable feats of strength and sexuality.

"Then there's this thing they call 'comedy.' But it is often difficult for me to understand, because the strangest aspect about this species is that they are never more amused than when they are observing someone else's embarrassment, discomfort, or injury. Out of all, injury is probably the most popular.

"Beyond their bizarre views of humor, there is another aspect about them that is most discomforting--they kill for pleasure. Most of the planet has advanced beyond the necessity to hunt for food. Now, they kill the creatures of their planet for a thing called 'sport.' From what I can understand, 'sport hunting' consists of ambushing mostly herbivorous, foraging animals at close proximity with high-powered projectile weapons.

"Hummph," muttered the captain, rolling an eye toward the ceiling.

"If that weren't enough," chuckled the communications officer, "they hang the heads of the creatures they kill on the walls of their abodes."

"No... Not really," said the navigator.

"Yes, they do. I swear on the never-still eyes of the Great One. It's a chilling thought, that below us is a species that kills for the sheer enjoyment of it, and possesses nuclear weapons. The best we can hope for is that they'll blow themselves up before they develop Thorian Drive and come visiting us."

"I think we've heard enough about this wonderful, little planet," said the captain, sitting up in his chair. "Navigator, plot us away, before some calamity befalls us and we find ourselves secretly displayed in some desert hanger, like they did with Gorth and his crew a few years back.

"Full T-Drive...."

****

THERE'S DARING, AND THEN THERE'S DAFT

Dec. 19, 1998

I was watching a special on "extreme sports" the other day--new ways of irreparably damaging your body while looking cool.

Tell me, what is it about man (and woman) that finds it necessary to undertake perilous enterprises for the sake of entertainment? Leaping from airplanes, scaling sheer rock walls, bunji-jumping, hang gliding, bull riding-- Lord, what happened to a picnic lunch on a riverbank and a rousing set of badminton?

I've noticed almost all the specials they show on television regarding these extreme sports are accompanied by beer or insurance commercials. The insurance is perfectly clear. I haven't been able to figure out whether the alcohol is to steady your nerves before hand or celebrate your victory over chance afterwards.

I can understand why the arena walls in bull riding events are covered with ads for Jack Daniels, Old Crow, and Budweiser. There's nothing like a little alcohol to dull the pain of setting a leg or a shoulder, or perhaps sewing on an ear.

Imagine climbing onto the back of 2,000 pounds of angry hoofs and horns--a creature whose only joy in life is throwing you off and stomping you into cowboy meat pie. If that wasn't enough, you don't even get a saddle. It's a wonder all those guys don't talk like Tiny Tim and aren't as sterile as a hitching post.

Another one of my favorites is those imdomintable souls who climb nearly vertical mountain cliffs with nothing more than a rosin bag in their back pocket. Poised like sinewy-muscled insects against sheer granite walls, they claw their way upwards across the unforgiving face of nature. With relentless, white-knuckled intensity they inch from crevice to crevice, knowing one wrong move, one failed grip, can mean certain death. What fun.

This is not one of those sports at which you can say, "Ooops, I missed. Give me another try." By the time you get the "ooops" out, you're already doing your Wiley Coyote imitation and nearing terminal velocity.

Then there's the bunji-jumpers... I especially liked the group who tied themselves together and jumped en masse off the bridge in Florida, never bothering to test the cord against the gravity they would exert.

"Looks strong enough to me. What do you think, dude?"

"Sure, no problem, man--looks good. Hey, toss me another Bud."

Of course, that particular episode went from bunji-jumping (SNAP), to bunji-flying (OOOPS), to bunji-crashing. Most of those who survived without permanent injury said they couldn't wait to do it again, which I think, says something more about mentality than courage.

Jumping out of perfectly good airplanes, or stepping out into an abyss with a flimsy Dacron kite attached to your back sure looks like fun, but I find myself weighing the highs and lows of the act.

On the positive side, I can expect to receive a momentary rush of adrenalin and a slightly inflated ego afterwards. On the negative side, I could possibly become an unidentifiable splotch of blood and hair on somebody's roof.

I don't know... I think I'll have a beer and cheer them from the couch.

THE UNWELCOME GUEST

March 30, 1999

The other day I ran into Rodge, my crazy hunting buddy from Mt. Ida. You might remember him from the disastrous turkey hunt I wrote about a few years back. Not surprisingly, he had experienced another "adventure" and had to relate it to me. Typically of Rodge, it's quite a story, and I thought I'd pass it on.

Rodge lives in a 60' by 12' mobile home just off Highway 27. It's not a bad place, except that it's decorated in early bachelor. Cast-off clothes, unwashed dishes and an assortment of beer cans are usually an accepted part of the ambience; nothing a good woman and a good cleaning couldn't fix. Rodge occasionally experiences both, though neither seem to last long enough to change that old hippie.

Rodge's latest problem dealt with an unwanted guest -- a rat. It seems this giant rat (Rodge's version) had decided to homestead in the walls of my friend's trailer. Now, I don't know if you've ever experienced this, but a rodent in the walls of your home can be a really disconcerting thing. It oftentimes doesn't matter how fastidious you are, they just seem to choose you, and they can be hell to get rid of.

Late at night Rodge would be having a bite to eat while watching TV, and he would hear that soft patter of padded feet across ceiling beams, a whisper of scratching, the rasping of tiny claws on wood, wallboard and insulation, as the creature gathered up the ingredients essential for a comfortable little nest. He tried traps; he caught the neighbor's cat. He tried poison; he killed two raccoons, a squirrel and a gecko lizard--but no rat. The little fellow was clever.

The rat would scratch inside the wall and Rodge would bang on the outside and yell at him. Terrible things, he called that rat: could have burned the ears off a sailor, but the furry little guy seemed unaffected and went right on building his nest.

Now, Rodge is not known for his patience or his decorum. (Remember, this is the guy who fishes with grenades.) Gradually it began to gnaw at him, the derned rodent was outsmarting him. It was eating his house, for God's sake, like it was a gingerbread cottage in some demented fairy tale!

It all came to a head one night: a sordid story of whiskey, vengeance and a twelve-gauge shotgun.

Rodge had been hunting earlier that day. Having capped off the event with a sixpack, he was sitting on the couch, working on his third Jack and water (very little water), cleaning his shotgun, when the scratching began.

Staring at the wall, he folded up his bore rod and put away the cleaning rags. "Dirty little $#@#$#," he muttered as he threw down the last of his drink and poured another--straight. As the scratching grew in intensity, he was sure that he could hear a squeaky, little voice laughing at him from behind the paneling. He took another drink. The voice and the scratching continued, growing louder. He began loading the gun, four rounds of number-eight shot, one in the chamber. He focused his bloodshot eyes as best he could on the area where the rasping, taunting sounds seemed to emanate from, and the barrel of the gun came around.

The cannon-like report of the weapon inside the room took even Rodge by surprise. Unfortunately, Rodge's approximation of the location of the rodent was a few inches off, for suddenly out of the smoking, jagged hole in the wall came a terrified Harry the Rat. It flew out of the hole and landed on the coffee table in front of my besotted friend. Disoriented and frightened, it bounded straight ahead onto Rodge's chest. Rodge let out a shriek and struggled to rise, knocking over the couch as he and the rat went head over heels behind it. In the interim, the shotgun discharged again, vaporizing the small chandelier on the ceiling and instantly installing a ten-inch skylight. Harry the Rat bounced off Rodge's forehead and headed down the hallway toward the bedrooms. Rodge was quick to recover, even as toasted as he was. He was a veteran; he'd been in combat before. He scrambled for his weapon and got off two rounds as the rat squealed and jagged down the corridor. The whiskey, however, didn't improve his aim. His first shot mortally wounded the air handler for the central air system. The second round went through the bathroom wall and disintegrated the top half of the commode. Harry the Rat made it to the bedroom.

The next day, in the process of cleanup (and $700.00 worth of repairs), Rodge found specks of blood in the hallway, but no sign of Harry anywhere. The scratching had ceased, and my friend began to savor his hard-won victory. He figured it was over, and it was--almost.

A few days later, Rodge began to sense a slightly unpleasant odor in his bedroom. A week later the area smelled like a men's room in a Guatemalan prison. It was fairly evident that Harry was getting revenge.

Rodge looked everywhere; he even pulled the paneling off a couple of walls. No Harry. He had almost given up, having taken to wearing deodorized cottonballs in his nose while he slept. One cold morning, he took his heavy army fatigue jacket out of the closet. Putting it on and walking outside, he noticed there seemed to be a particular aura of dead rat about him. The neighbor's coon dogs had taken to following and yipping at him.

The cold wind whipped across his face. He shivered and stuck his hands in his pockets....

The little fellow must have had a great sense of humor, for in his last moments he had crawled into his nemesis' favorite coat. It must have been a sight, seeing Rodge jerk his hand out of his pocket, rip that jacket off, then have to fight the coon dogs for it.

I'd have to say the last laugh went to Harry.

****

HEADSTONES AND HISTORY

June 4, 1999

You can't drive far on a rural road without, at some point, passing a local cemetery. I had cause to stop at one the other day. It was an interesting and enlightening experience, and I thought I'd share it with you.

As I walked across the manicured grass, punctuated by a rainbow of flowers, I studied the headstones around me. I was amazed by the insight I was given of those souls who had come to this land before me. It was an exercise in history and a lesson into the character of the American. I found testimonials to courage and faith, and kindness, memorials to teachers and preachers, to masons, doctors and soldiers, and the loving memory etched in the stone was nearly always the same: that those folks had served their nation, their God, and their fellow man, to the best of their ability.

Many a headstone reflected the pride those men and women carried for their country, and the honor they felt having served when their name was called.

Floyd William Slatter, Airman First Class WWII. 1910-1984

Mary Beth Campbell, Lieutenant R.N. U.S. Army, WWII. 1913-1990

Terry Peterson, Captain, 101st Airborne, Vietnam. 1947-1970

I could almost see them in their crisply pressed uniforms, saluting from the train on that brilliant morning, as their family and friends waved and cried, and whispered, "Godspeed home." The dates on the stones told that some returned. For others, their loved ones were left with only the memory of those proud, bright faces smiling back at them... Americans, real Americans, one and all.

There was Fred Sanders, born in 1893. His wife Lydia was born in 1897. They found each other, fell in love, and raised a family, but Lydia died when she was forty-three. The dates on the single tombstone told the story of how he had waited forty more years to lie beside her once again.

William and Claudia Pellston were both seventeen when they were married in 1926. They spent the next sixty years together as man and wife, and when the sun rises each day now, the first rays that touch that little knoll still find them together.

In a time when marriages seem to last about as long as a head cold, when people rotate their mates like they do the tires on their cars, and devotion to one's country no longer seems to be in fashion, it was remarkably refreshing to discover loyalty and love that had lasted a lifetime;

to be reminded of honor and courage, and pride in these United States.

Walking through that stone garden I was also reminded that the weave which has bound the tapestry of this land for so long is not technological achievement or grand edifice. It is not cultural autonomy or even the independence of race and gender, but rather it is an amalgam of integrity, responsibility, and spirit; for without these qualities in its people, no nation can stand strong.

I recommend that each of us take pause at a rural, roadside cemetery and stroll through the headstones of history, so we might remember that it is the individual character of the people within a nation which lend character to that land.

Hold fast to your faith and your honor Middle America, as your forefathers did, for I have discovered what I suspected all along: that you are the pith and the marrow of this land.

****

About the Author

Michael Reisig was born in Enid, Oklahoma, in 1948. The first son of a military family, he graduated high school in Tampa, Florida, and attended St. Petersburg Junior College.

After college, he relocated to the Florida Keys, establishing a commercial diving business and traveling extensively throughout the southern hemisphere--diving, treasure hunting, adventuring, and writing of his travels.

Reisig presently resides in the Ouachita Mountains of Arkansas. He is the "Ouachita Outdoors" editor for the *Mena Star*, and continues to pen his novels.

Reisig's first novel, *The New Madrid Run*, is a tale of desperate survival on an altered planet: *In the aftermath of a global cataclysm caused by a shift in the earth's poles, a handful of survivors face the terrible elements of a changed world as they navigate a battered sailboat from the ruins of Florida into the hills of Arkansas via a huge rift in the continent (the New Madrid fault). They survive fierce storms and high seas pirates only to make landfall and discover the greatest challenge of all....*

The Hawks of Kamalon, Reisig's latest novel, is a fast-paced tale of interplanetary adventure and intrigue: In the summer of 1944, a small squadron of British and American aircraft depart at dawn on a long-range strike into the heart of Germany, but as the squadron crosses the English Channel, it disappears.... *You're about to be introduced to a band of reluctant heroes: a motley group of brawlers, lovers, and pretenders--fighter pilots--champions, one and all, for a desperate nation somewhere on the other side of the Milky Way.*

Watch for these novels on audio cassette by Books in Motion

Visit Michael Reisig's website at www.michael-reisig.com and read a chapter or two of his books.